The Illustrated Library of

NATURE

VOLUME 12

OCEAN
LIFE–(cont.)

PETS

The American Museum of Natural History

Cooperated in the publication
of this edition.

The opinions expressed by authors are their own and
do not necessarily reflect the policy of the Museum.

The Illustrated Library of
NATURE

THIS PICTORIAL ENCYCLOPEDIA of natural history and ecology depicts the relationships of all living organisms to each other and between them and their environments. Original manuscript from the *Doubleday Nature Programs* plus new articles and illustrations are included in this edition.

H. S. STUTTMAN CO., INC., Publishers
New York, N.Y., 10016

Contents

VOLUME 12

Larvae of the **langouste,** or **spiny lobster,** look very little like the mature adult, with its long antennae and hard, prickly-spined shell. The larvae have flat, transparent, leaflike bodies, with long legs. Their shells harden after about six weeks.

Whips of Coral

A T TIMES A FISHERMAN, angling near the bottom of the mouth of a
bay, will find his hook and line snared in a strange, orange-red
mass that someone may identify for him as a "sea whip". He may well
decide that the growth is some unusual kind of seaweed, and he is unlikely to guess the truth: the sea whip is a coral colony, somewhat related to the more usual forms just described.

The sea whips found along the U. S. Atlantic coast, and in bays such
as the Chesapeake and Delaware, are known as gorgonians, because
they sometimes resemble the mass of snakes that crowned the head of
the mythical Gorgon Medusa. The most common sea whip in bay regions is *Leptogorgia*. Close inspection of a dried whip shows tiny pits
along the surface that in life are occupied by small polyps—minute
translucent animals each with eight feathery tentacles. The polyps do
not contact each other bodily; they have thin tubular connections from
which new polyps sprout. Each polyp deposits its quota of the tinted
horny material of which the colony is composed, and which maintains
it in a state of slow but continuous growth. Entirely new colonies are
initiated when swimming larvae are carried by ocean currents to new
regions where they can settle and grow.

Jellyfish Are "Jet-propelled"

J ELLYFISH AND SEA ANEMONES are closely related. Both have saclike
bodies, and a single opening to the body cavity, surrounded by
tentacles, is a distinctive feature of both. But in anemones the mouth
is uppermost, while in jellyfish it is on the undersurface. Of course,
anemones cannot swim and only creep slowly about the bottom, but
jellyfish are swimmers and move by contraction of the "umbrella" which
produces a pumping action that is a kind of jet propulsion.

Dactylometra is a quite common jellyfish in bays and estuaries, and

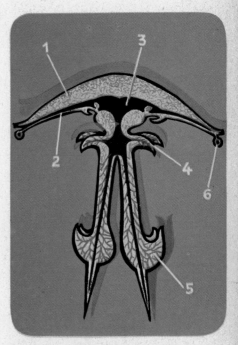

Although the **jellyfish** is related to the
anemone, it would be hard to confuse
the two. Unlike the anemone, the
jellyfish has its stomach (3), mouth (4)
and oral canal (5) on its underside.
While the anemone barely creeps
along the ocean floor, the jellyfish
propels itself energetically through the
water by pumping its "umbrella" (1-2),
keeping upright by signals from its
sensory tentacles(6).

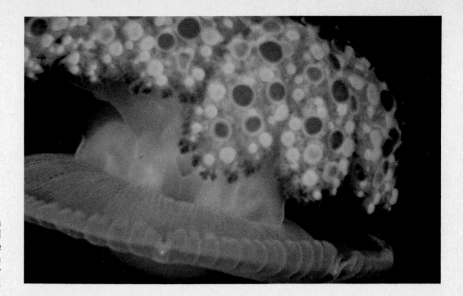

The umbrella of this **bay jellyfish** is a beautiful sight, but those colorful jewel-like circles are far from mere decoration; in reality, they contain very potent stinging cells, similar to those on the tentacles.

it is also found in the open ocean. The "umbrella" of this large pink and white creature may be as much as eight inches wide, with about forty tentacles streaming several feet below. Scattered over the surface of the umbrella are small bumps which contain groups of stinging cells similar to those which are to be found in great numbers on the tentacles. *Dactylometra* produces a very painful sting.

About the rim of the umbrella are eight sense organs which show up clearly as white dots. These simple structures indicate to the animal when it is tilted and, should you attempt to turn a jellyfish over in the water, you will find that it will quickly right itself. Each sense organ contains a mass of tiny white "pebbles" which roll about in a small cavity. These exert pressure upon nerve endings that in turn tell the jellyfish on which side of the umbrella it must pump faster in order to regain an even keel.

Sometimes, in late summer, bays become so filled with *Dactylometra* that swimming becomes a hazardous pastime. They clog nets and wash up on beaches, where they evaporate and leave nothing but the thinnest film on the sand. In northern waters, the same is true with the large, red sun jellyfish, *Cyanea*. Exceptionally large specimens of *Cyanea* have been recorded as having diameters of seven feet or more, and tentacles well over one hundred feet in length! The more dangerous Portuguese man-of-war actually is *not* a jellyfish, but a colony of individual polyp-like animals floating in a gas bag.

Of Names and Worms

THE NAMES WHICH MAY ADEQUATELY DESCRIBE an animal for a scientist are quite often almost meaningless to the non-biologist. An exception is *Stylochus zebra*; this is a flatworm that is found frequently in empty whelk shells or in shells inhabited by hermit crabs, and its conspicuous stripes are immediately reminiscent of the horselike animal from the plains of Africa.

Members of this group are among the largest of marine flatworms, and the habits of some of them have economic consequences that make them important. Several species of *Stylochus* enter living oysters by creeping between the open valves of the mollusk, and once inside, they feed upon the oyster's flesh.

Near the front end of one of these flatworms is a pair of short, stubby tentacles. Each of these sensory organs contains two groups of primitive eyespots that are capable of discerning only the difference between light and dark. Other isolated eyespots are found along the margins of the broad body, and probably to some degree assist in directing the animal toward the dark shaded regions where it usually prefers to live.

To those biologists who study estuaries, it seems that bays are filled with worms and shrimps, so great is the number and variety of these two forms of life. As bays generally have a muddy, or sand-and-mud bottom, burrowing forms of life are plentiful. If some of this mud is scooped up from the floor of the bay and examined, dozens or hundreds of worms are found in each cubic foot. Most of them never reach an inch in length. One of these little worms is *Goniada*, a slender animal with a cone-shaped head at the tip of which are borne four tiny antennae. On each segment it bears a pair of paddle-like appendages used in moving about and in "breathing". On the undersurface of its head is a mouth, inside of which is a proboscis (a sort of tongue) fitted with several rows of horny teeth. The worm lives in loosely constructed tubes in the mud, devouring microscopic plants and animals and decaying matter. Why should we consider it here? Because it is typical of the hundreds of small bottom forms that in one way or another play important roles in the complex animal population of the bay.

A larger but very similar worm is *Nereis,* the sand worm. This animal, also called a clamworm because it occasionally occupies empty clam shells, is usually well known to fishermen and visitors at the shore, for it is very common. It lives in cluttered bottoms where shells, timbers, rocks and debris afford protection. Under these objects *Nereis* constructs burrows from which it emerges at night to seek food.

Although *Nereis* is a member of the same group of segmented worms to which the earthworm belongs, it differs from its land relative by having tentacles, jaws, eyes and swimming and breathing appendages on each segment. Its senses are acute; not only do its simple eyes distinguish light and shade, but tentacles and bristles indicate changes in pressure and movement.

When feeding or defending itself, *Nereis* throws a muscular proboscis out through its mouth. A pair of large, sharp jaws at the tip of the proboscis close with a pincer action on the prey, and the proboscis is withdrawn into the mouth; the food is received into a muscular pharynx

Marine flatworms often crawl into abandoned shells of other sea creatures. Sometimes a flatworm will attempt to inhabit a living shellfish, such as an oyster, and will gradually destroy the original owner of the shell.

Not all worms are slow movers.
Although attached to one spot, the
feather-duster worm will snap its
feathery tentacles back into its tube
with lightning speed if threatened.

and swallowed. The jaws of large specimens can inflict a painful nip on a human hand.

House-building Worms

CHIMNEY-LIKE TUBES rising from muddy and sandy portions of the bay bottom sometimes exist in surprising profusion. Upon close examination these prove to be tubes constructed of a very tough material, covered on the outside with fragments of shell, algae, bits of wood, pebbles and any other foreign materials that might be found lying on the floor of the bay. One of these tubes projects several inches above the bottom, but two feet or more beneath the sand. If the water is shallow and some sort of viewing device is used, you may be treated to the sight of the animal that makes this shelter; it is far more attractive and graceful than the crude nature of the tube would lead you to suspect.

Diopatra is its name, and it is called the "plumed worm" in recognition of its long, slender tentacles and the scarlet, treelike gills arising from each segment. This animal is iridescent, and as it emerges from its tube, bending to grope in search of food, it is "transformed" as the light which falls on it is reflected as ever-changing metallic shades of blue and green. Prolonged observation may reveal the tube-building activity; for when *Diopatra* is extended, it may happen across a bit of shell which it will promptly pick up and fasten to the outer portion of the tube.

Although an adult *Diopatra* does not completely emerge from its tube, it is nevertheless liable to fall prey to other sea creatures. But those that wish to make a meal of this particular worm need to move quickly—because it can turn around in its tube and descend like a flash several feet below the surface of the sand.

Fishing lines sometimes get snagged on objects which, when they are pulled to the surface of the bay, look at first glance for all the world like a mass of coral. It may be that real coral *does* grow in the bay—but this particular catch is something quite different. It is a colony of worms.

These peculiar little creatures, known as *Hydroids* or feather-duster worms, are fixed in one spot and cannot move about. As they grow, they construct tubes of calcium deposits that afford them nearly complete protection. The tubes are white, coiled or twisted, and rise up in masses from shells or rocks to which they are fastened. In the opening of each tube can be seen a crown of feathery tentacles, red, orange, brown or black. Each "crown" consists of about three dozen tentacles, and they serve a double purpose. The tentacles are breathing organs, and they are also an essential part of the equipment for obtaining food. On them are cilia, which beat rapidly and force a current of water down toward the mouth. The "feathers" also produce a slime that traps any food particles that come into contact with them.

Small black dots on the tentacles are eyespots, which seem to be more than mere detectors of light and dark, because these creatures can be seen to react to moving objects. When a colony of these animals is in an aquarium, the wave of a hand in front of the glass is sufficient to cause all the animals to contract into their tubes.

One part of the feathery crown is different from all the other plumes: it is a bulb on a stalk, the end of which is so constructed that mud and debris stick to it. When the animal is frightened, it pops back into its tube and plugs the entrance with this bulb, disguising the opening.

These worms and their close relatives may be serious pests to those who sail the oceans, for they often grow in huge colonies on the bottoms of ships. If many such "fouling" animals attach themselves to a ship's hull they affect the speed and handling of a vessel. More fuel is consumed, and in time of war when ships need to be speedy, long-running and easy to turn, the fouling can be dangerous. Industry has produced anti-fouling paints which are very effective in discouraging the growth of these and other pests.

Feather-duster worms retain their eggs in special brood pouches for a short time, but after they are fertilized the embryos develop into free-swimming larvae. About two weeks later each larva attaches to a bare surface and begins to form a tube which increases in size as the animal grows. When a mass of worm tubes has been made, many other animals arrive to live on or in the tubes.

A moss animal colony characteristically covers the surface of the tubes with small units, each of which contains one individual moss animal, or bryozoan, and which in total look like miniature cobblestones. Other worms, perhaps *Goniada,* construct mud tubes among the larger tubes. Snails and yellow sponges encrust the surface, and shrimps and other worms inhabit any vacant tubes that they discover.

Sea Urchins Are Living Pincushions

THE SEA URCHIN is another animal typical of the lower regions of bays where sea water is not too diluted by fresh water from the outflow of rivers. All spiny-skinned animals—sea urchins, starfish, brittle stars and sea cucumbers—are animals that are found only in salt water and have no freshwater relatives. They may be abundant along seacoasts and in the mouths of bays, but soon disappear if the salt content is appreciably reduced.

The purple sea urchin, *Arbacia,* is one of the most abundant of these forms. It is a purplish brown, with stout, reddish brown spines. The spines on the upper regions are long and cylindrical, while those on the undersurface are flattened and end in broad, flat tips.

The ten clusters of tube feet surrounding the mouth provide this animal with an efficient means of moving about, and of breathing and feeling. They are directed by weak muscles, but water pressure is the

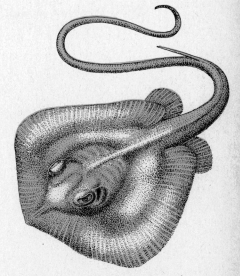

Often populating estuaries along with other forms of marine life, the **skate,** a simple, flattened fish, has a skeleton made of cartilage rather than of true bone. Its body structure reveals this fish to be a relative of the shark.

This is not an underwater porcupine but a many-spined **sea urchin.** Thriving in sea water, it will survive in bays as long as the waters are salty enough, protected by its spiny armor from many animals that might attempt to devour it.

Shallow waters contain many kinds of shellfish, whose empty shells often wash up onto the shore. Many of the living shellfish are eagerly sought and highly valued as food. The **soft-shell clam,** the **pismo clam** and the **quahog** (or **hard-shell**) **clam** are all popular with seafood eaters, and the shells of the latter were used by American Indians to make wampum (bead-money). **Mussel shells** may be ribbed or smooth, but variety of shape and size is more pronounced in the clams: for example, in the tiny **coquina,** the elongated **razor clam** and the huge **geoduck.** For the most unusual habits, however, we must turn to the **shipworm clam,** whose shells form a jawlike, wood-boring apparatus, and to the **piddock clam,** which can bore into soft rock, clay and other types of hard bottoms.

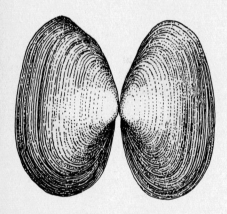

SOFT-SHELL CLAM

real force that makes them move and take hold of surrounding surfaces by suction.

The sea urchin's body is a complex system of tubes, valves and muscular bulbs able to build up considerable water pressure. Depending upon the water pressure within the system, the tube feet are extended or drawn back. Together with the spines, which have ball-and-socket joints and their own muscles, the tube feet provide a most unusual method of slow-but-sure motion. The animals wedge themselves into rock crevices with tube feet and spines so securely that no wave can dislodge them.

The undersurface has a protruding central beak consisting of five jaws. The mouth parts of a sea urchin are wonderfully complex, and were named "Aristotle's lantern" by an imaginative biologist. By means of many joints and muscles, the jaws can be rotated, extended, closed and drawn back as the urchin scrapes away at the rocks to remove any useful encrusting vegetation and decaying matter.

Arranged over the spherical skeleton between the spines are stalked, three-toothed structures that have several functions. The shape and size of the teeth differ and some have poison glands. Depending upon the structure of the teeth, they defend the sea urchins against large or small foes, seize animals for food and remove debris which might accumulate.

The Best-known Animal—the Oyster

T HE OYSTER IS ONE of the most common of all estuary dwellers. This bivalve mollusk has remained relatively unchanged for millions of years. In a sense it can be called the world's best-known animal, for the oyster has been the subject of more research than any other creature.

Marine mollusks include clams, mussels, oysters, snails, squids, octopuses, and even this odd-looking species, *Peltodoris atromaculata.*

RIBBED BAY MUSSEL

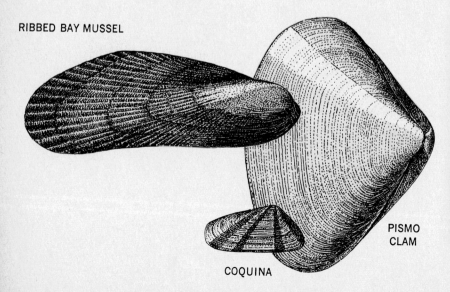

COQUINA

PISMO CLAM

In some estuaries it carpets the bottom with hundreds of thousands of individuals. We shall not discuss the oyster here, other than to say that it is an estuarine animal and that the free-swimming larvae must find clean and suitable areas where they can attach themselves to something hard. Because so many problems beset this shelled animal, and because it is valuable commercially, there is the necessity of further study of the oyster and its enemies. Any plant or animal that destroys the oyster, eats it, smothers it or prevents its attachment, has been studied in this connection, and the research continues.

The total value of the world's annual oyster harvest is immense; to give some idea of the importance of the oyster to those who farm it—one of the smallest states of the United States, with few oyster beds compared with some other regions, has an annual catch varying in value between three and five million dollars.

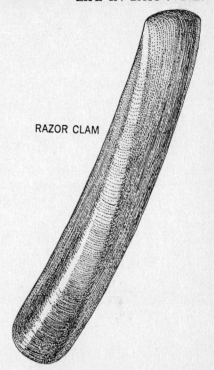

RAZOR CLAM

Drills Are Carnivorous Snails

ONE OF THE ANIMALS that affects young oysters is the oyster drill. There are two major species, *Urosalpinx* being the most important because of its large numbers. This yellowish or brownish snail has an elongated, sharply tapered shell with about six spiral turns, crossed by rounded ribs and raised lines that result in a vague crisscross pattern.

Urosalpinx uses its rasping, filelike, horny tongue to bore holes into young oysters. The living oyster is then sucked out through the hole and the snail moves on to another waiting victim. Its tastes are varied, and while fixed oysters are the easiest prey, it will attack other kinds of clams and snails. Any mollusk will fall victim as long as its shell is not too thick and the drill cannot be dislodged.

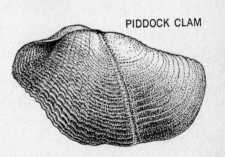

PIDDOCK CLAM

QUAHOG CLAM

SHIPWORM CLAM

GEODUCK CLAM

One mollusk without a shell is the exotic-looking **sea hare.** With an arched back and anterior tentacles that could be taken for ears, this fantastic creature may reach a length of up to two feet.

Next to the starfish it is the worst destroyer of oysters, but as starfish live only in salt waters, the drill is the most serious predator in the brackish waters of an estuary. Still, oyster drills also have a limit for dilution of sea water; if it is a little less than a fifty per cent mixture, the drill is absent. Oysters can live in water that is eighty-five per cent fresh, so quite a few of them are free from their two major enemies, drills and starfish.

Snails of many types carpet the bottom and shores of bays. When the tides go out over mud flats, hundreds of thousands of mud snails are left exposed to creep about the moist mud, seeking decaying food and leaving the surface furrowed with their trails. Great conchs, or whelks, lie buried in the sand and mud bottoms with only tips of their shells protruding to indicate the presence of snails that may be nine inches long.

Often attached to these large mollusks are shallow, clinging shells that do not show the typical spiralling of most snails. They are slipper shells, *Crepidula,* and each is occupied by a snail which fits under a shelflike ledge extending from the narrow part of the shell. *Crepidula* shells are shaped according to the object on which the snail grows. Once it adheres to an object, it may lift the shell and crawl about slightly, but always returns to the one and only spot where it can clamp down with an absolutely tight seal. This is the *Crepidula's* method of preventing drying if exposed to air, and of defending itself against predators. Sometimes these shells may be found adhering to each other, forming a chain of individuals.

The microscopic food that *Crepidula* feeds upon is strained and separated; one-celled algae are eaten continuously, while other food is stored in a pouch for periodic feeding.

When *Crepidula* is pried up from its base, yellow egg masses can sometimes be found left on the surface. If you examine a few of them under a powerful magnifying glass you can see the embryos turning around inside the eggs. These eggs are contained in groups of several dozen in membranous, transparent sacs, each of which is attached to the base by jelly-like strings. When the young hatch out they are free-swimming forms, typical of marine snail larvae. As they develop into snails, they first become males and fertilize eggs of females, and later become females and go about the process of egg-laying.

Handsome Slugs and Winged Snails

Sea slug is hardly an appropriate name for the beautiful, shell-less marine snails that can be found along many seashores. These creatures, often brilliantly hued, have some form of breathing apparatus on their upper surfaces. The variety is considerable; in some it is composed of filaments; in others it is leaflike; in yet others it is balloon-like, star-shaped or highly branched and feathery.

Aeolis is a common sea slug, usually found in association with algae, sea anemones or hydroids. It feeds upon these organisms and its relationship with certain hydroids is a strange one. In some fashion not yet understood it manages to devour the individual polyps without their sting cells discharging. These cells then become separated from the rest of the food material, pass through the walls of the digestive system of the sea slug and migrate out to its respiratory filaments, and arrange themselves in such a way as to form a defensive system for the mollusk. Perhaps in ages past this situation was the first case of captured armament being used by the enemy!

Sea slugs often take on the hue of the material on which they feed. This is not due to any control over their pigmentation; it is simply because their tissues are almost perfectly transparent. Regardless of how it occurs, this "imitation" of the background must serve to some degree as a protective mechanism.

A biologist working in an estuary will never predict the forms of life likely to be present or absent at a given time, because the environment is so often subject to extreme variation in a short space of time—even as

(above)
Winglike fins steer the delicate **pteropods,** or **winged snails,** through the waters in vast groups. Forming part of the ocean plankton, they are most populous in northern regions, where the great whales feed on them.

(left)
Related to and somewhat resembling the cuttlefish, the **spirula** has a coiled shell of many chambers that is almost completely enclosed by the soft parts of the animal.

short a period as an hour can bring about a considerable change of conditions. An example of a surprising event in a temperate zone bay was the discovery of strange swimming snails, pteropods that usually are confined to Arctic waters. What vagaries of coastal currents had brought them so far south could not be explained; but here they were, in appreciable numbers, at the mouth of a bay far from their normal frigid environment.

Pteropods of this type have no shell, although one is present in embryonic stages. Of two pairs of tentacles growing on the head, one has a pair of rudimentary eyes. Two large winglike fins extend from the body, and penetrating into these fins are branches of the animal's liver.

Pteropods are carnivorous, and well equipped to "process" their captured prey into food; besides having jaws they have tough, rasplike tongues. In their turn, they are fed upon in enormous quantities by the Greenland right whale, one of the great marine mammals that derives nourishment by straining plankton from the sea. The winged snails seem to live together in huge streams, and demonstrate a periodic vertical migration in ascending to the surface at night and sinking into the depths during daylight hours.

The Blue-eyed Scallop

A BIVALVE MOLLUSK commonly found in bays, well known because of its commercial importance, is the scallop: *Pecten*. Scallops are unusual mollusks, for although clamlike, they can swim rapidly and look back at you with thirty or forty brilliant blue eyes!

The two shells, or valves, of a scallop are not identical; the more deeply curved one is the "bottom", while the flatter one represents the "top". Because it makes an excellent place for barnacles, tube worms,

The **scallop** appears odd for several reasons. Its upper and lower shells are not symmetrical, giving it a protruding lower "lip." Numerous tiny animals attach themselves to its shell in a haphazard fashion. And the scallop stares at you with at least thirty bright blue eyes!

hydroids and moss animals to settle, these creatures provide the scallop with some degree of protection by making it resemble the sea bed.

When a scallop is at rest its shells open, displaying many sensory tentacles and two rows of blue eyes on each half of the mantle. These eyes are well developed, and possess many of the same basic structures we have in our own eyes. All the eyes in each row are connected to a common nerve; such an arrangement of eyes should make it easy for the scallop to detect any motion in objects within its field of vision even though the object is unlikely to be seen very clearly. If you watch scallops in an aquarium you will see that they close their shells violently with the least movement which occurs outside the tank, but when the movement ceases, they open once more.

When scallops are in a tank with a starfish, a natural enemy, or are irritated in some way, they swim. Slow swimming from place to place is quite different from escape swimming. In the first, the valves open and close rapidly, forcing the water out near the hinge, so that the animal moves with eyes and tentacles foremost. In escape swimming the action is quite different—the water drawn in is shot out through the free edge of the shells, and the animal goes hinge foremost. This latter type of swimming is accomplished with such force that the scallop is quite capable of rising clear above the surface.

The rapid opening and closing of the two valves requires a special muscle, which is more familiar to most of us than we might suspect. It is the part of the scallop that is usually eaten, the rest of the animal being discarded. This muscle is large and powerful and is divided into two unequal parts. The larger part is used to keep the shell closed over long periods. This last is the muscle that a starfish must work against when attempting to open a scallop. When the muscles are relaxed, an elastic ligament snaps open the shell with no effort on the part of the animal.

Large populations of scallops are often found in shallow bays and over mud flats. Many tons are dredged up by fishermen to satisfy seafood enthusiasts.

Horseshoe Crabs Are Living Fossils

For 350 million years, a marine relative of spiders has lived in bays, estuaries and shallow seas. It has changed somewhat over the ages, but in form it is still very much like its ancient ancestors. Biologists know it as *Limulus polyphemus;* everyone else calls it a horseshoe crab. It is not a crab, nor is it related to crabs, except that it is classified under the same major group which includes crustaceans, insects and spiders. Four species of this animal are alive today. Three of them are found in the western Pacific and Indian oceans and one in the Atlantic Ocean. We can feel fortunate in being able to see, and perhaps to study, this relic of prehistoric times.

A favorite place for the female **horseshoe crab** to deposit her eggs is the sandy beach of an estuary. The eggs are fertilized, and a month later the baby horseshoe crab is hatched and slowly makes its way back to the water. Only after several moults does the characteristic spike tail begin to appear in the growing animal.

Floral life under the sea is as varied and interesting as the animal life. The **sea moss,** or **bryopsis,** and the **plumeria,** or **featherweed,** are two feathery-looking plants with soft, delicate appearances. About twenty species of sea moss are known, all with fine filaments that branch and rebranch. Plumeria thrives in cool Atlantic and Pacific waters and is easily recognized because of its red hues. Both **sea lettuce** and **rockweed** (opposite page), although very different in shape, grow in bays throughout the world. Chlorophyll makes the sea lettuce green, indicating its use of sunlight to synthesize food, in the same way that land-bound green plants nourish themselves. Budlike air bladders on the rockweed's branches keep it from scraping along the ocean floor as waves pound over it. **Irish moss** has uses outside the sea, being widely employed as a jelling agent in home cooking and as a source of industrial chemicals. Turtles, sea horses, and other marine animals feed heavily on **turtle grass,** which may grow to four feet in the quiet shallow waters of estuaries.

As spring warmth soaks into the bay, *Limulus* comes in from deeper water toward the shores, moving slowly across the bottom like a miniature armored tank, or occasionally swimming upside down close to the surface. The swimming action is accomplished by a fluttering of the leaflike gills under the animal's abdomen. The males precede the females to the beach, sometimes by a week or two. When the females arrive pairing takes place, and each female deposits its greenish eggs in a shallow sandy nest at high tide during the new and full moons. Sperm are liberated over the eggs and fertilization is accomplished. The pair then moves on to construct another nest and lay more eggs. About two weeks after fertilization a break appears in the outer covering of each egg, and an inner transparent membrane becomes inflated with sea water. At this stage the embryo can be seen moving about within its confining envelope. After a month the membrane splits and the larval horseshoe crab escapes into the water.

Resembling other members of the group of joint-footed animals with outer skeletons, *Limulus* periodically sheds its hard outer covering in order to grow. Before the old casing is discarded a new, soft, wrinkled skin will already have formed beneath it. Then the old covering splits along the outer curve of the "horseshoe" and the animal begins to emerge. The new skin loses its wrinkles as it expands, and when the crab has entirely emerged from its former skeleton, it is considerably larger. Once the horseshoe crab is fully grown this periodical "change of clothing" is no longer essential; consequently, some of the large, old specimens obtained in bays are encrusted with moss animals, hydroids, barnacles and algae.

Limulus is a bottom feeder, devouring great quantities of sand worms, proboscis worms and many kinds of clams. Although its claws are weak,

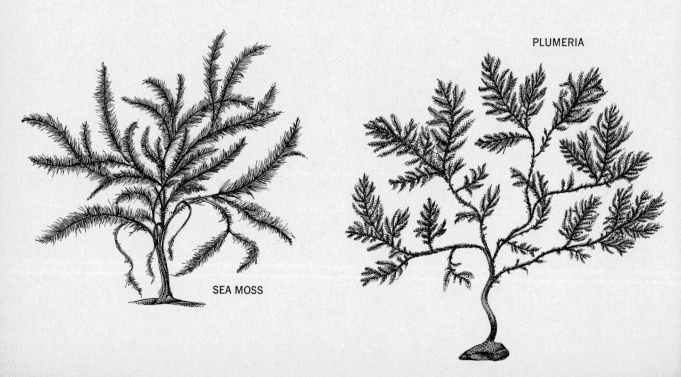

PLUMERIA

SEA MOSS

it has powerful crushing structures at the bases of its hind legs which are capable of smashing a clam shell, freeing the fleshy part of the mollusk to serve as an easily swallowed meal.

Armored Crustaceans Live Everywhere in the Sea

CRUSTACEANS VARY IN SIZE from the giant spider crab of Japanese waters to microscopic "shrimps" which comprise a large percentage of the plankton that drifts freely in surface waters. Lobsters and crabs are commercially valuable, but no crustaceans are more important than the small, almost invisible, floating forms. The reason for this lies in their immense numbers, and in the fact that whale-bone whales, menhaden, whale sharks, manta rays and many more of the largest or most numerous marine animals rely upon plankton for their only food. These small crustaceans may not make up 100 per cent of the plankton, but they often are in the majority.

If you are fortunate enough to have the use of a microscope, you have a splendid opportunity to become really familiar with planktonic plants and animals. All that is needed, besides a microscope and glass slides, is a conical net made out of fine cloth. This is towed through the water for a while, then is pulled up and allowed to drain. When a soupy mass forms in the bottom of the net, it is transferred to a bottle with a little sea water. It is impossible to predict with any accuracy what you will discover when a drop of this concentrated marine life is examined under a microscope; for the plants and animals making up plankton are so numerous and different that marine biologists continually find entirely new species.

Plankton is abundant in nearly every large body of water, but no-

TURTLE GRASS

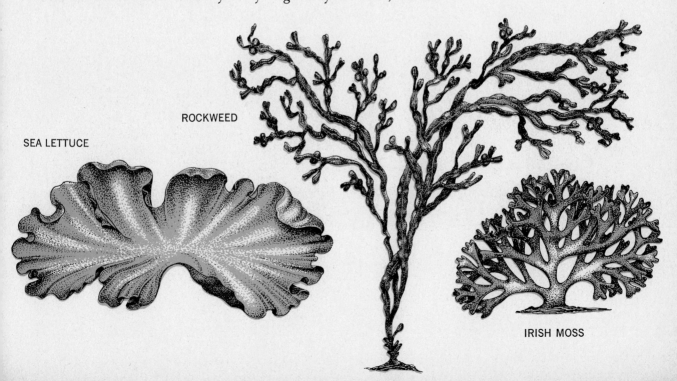

SEA LETTUCE

ROCKWEED

IRISH MOSS

where is it more densely concentrated than in bays and estuaries. Here particular kinds of planktonic crustaceans are found, well adapted to the rigorous environment. These small crustaceans, or "shrimps", are of many basic types, but one common type is the copepod.

Copepods Are Basic Food for Most Bay Animals

COPEPODS ARE STREAMLINED AQUATIC ANIMALS only a small fraction of an inch in length. They swim by rapidly jerking their long antennae, while their tails serve as rudders. The copepods found in inland fresh waters are active swimmers, and their antennae are rather short and powerful. They must swim constantly because fresh water is less dense than salt water, and fresh water animals in general have less buoyancy than those found in the sea. Salt water copepods found far out in the sea are not such active swimmers, but rely upon long feathery antennae to hold them up with a minimum effort.

As you might expect then, brackish water copepods such as inhabit estuaries are midway between fresh and salt water types—not only as regards their structure but also the way they behave. Those few species of copepods best adapted to estuaries may occur in such vast numbers as to defy the imagination. In one recent plankton tow, a gallon bottle became packed solid with nothing but one species of bay copepod.

Despite the fact that surface-feeding animals eat millions, copepods maintain the same enormous numbers due to their efficient and rapid reproduction. Many of the females can be seen carrying one or two bumpy sacs full of eggs on either side of their tails. The eggs hatch out quickly into small swimming forms not easily recognizable as copepods, but after a series of moults are full grown and ready to reproduce again.

Slim tendrils anchor the saclike **egg cases** of skates and rays to rocks and vegetation. Containing large numbers of eggs, these sacs are imaginatively named "sea purses" or "mermaids' purses."

Skeleton Shrimps Are Natural Boxers

THE SKELETON SHRIMP, *Caprella,* is considerably larger than a copepod, and is very common in bay and estuarine waters. This animal,
seldom more than a half-inch in length, is amusing to watch; yet it is a
ferocious creature which captures all small animals that come too close.

Caprella is slender, with long antennae, powerful grasping claws and
a tiny button of an abdomen. It holds on to seaweeds and hydroids with
its rear legs, keeping its body erect. Its claws are held ready and partly
extended, and the animal continually weaves and bobs about in the
manner of a shadow-boxer. When a smaller animal swims by, *Caprella*
reaches its claws out faster than the eye can follow and seizes the
prey, which it then proceeds to tear apart and swallow.

When skeleton shrimps move from place to place they resemble the
familiar inch worm, looping along by first holding on with their front
claws, then bringing up their hind legs, and once again extending their
claws. Often they are so well camouflaged as to resemble closely the
area in which they live.

If polarized light is used to observe or to photograph *Caprella*'s leg,
the muscular structural details show up very clearly through a microscope. The range of spectral hues is useful as well as striking. Where
very thin tissues running in different directions lie one above the other
this can be seen with complete clarity, despite their nearly complete
transparency, since at least three distinct hues will be revealed where
in ordinary light almost nothing could be seen.

Outer skeletons of all crustaceans, insects and spiders are made of a
horny material, and in the crustaceans this is often strengthened with
deposits of lime. Joints are formed by a thinning of the skeleton. As
this covering is not elastic and stretchable, it must be shed from time
to time to allow for growth. In order to move the jointed pieces which
compose the skeleton of one of these animals, a system of many separate
muscles must be developed. These muscles extend and retract various
sections by being stretched across the joints *inside* the skeleton. Our
own joints are moved in a somewhat similar fashion, but our muscles
are stretched over the joints *outside* the skeleton.

The bulging head of *Caprella* and many other animals related to it
(insects) is no sign of intelligence, but rather that they are "muscle-
heads". Their jointed jaws and other working mouth parts must be
moved separately, but are too small to contain muscles powerful enough
to tear into food. The muscles, therefore, are anchored to the top and
sides of the head.

How a Shrimp Changes its Tone

NEARLY ALL CRUSTACEANS are marked in one fashion or another,
and while some of these hues may originate deep within the

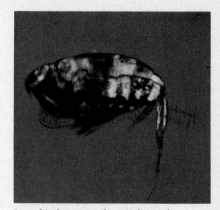

Found in huge numbers in bays, the common **copepod** swims by jerking its two long, downward-pointing antennae. Its tail acts as a rudder, helping to keep the animal moving constantly through the water.

body, many of them are found closely associated with the outer skeleton. Crustaceans may be red, orange, yellow, violet, green, blue, brown or black, but not all in any one kind of animal.

These pigments are usually contained in highly branched cells; the branches contract and expand in response to changes of brightness of the surrounding light. When the branches expand, the animal seems to be the hue of the cells, but when the branches contract, the pigment is confined to a small central spot in each cell and the whole tone of the animal becomes lighter as a result. Even blinded crustaceans exhibit this kind of reaction to some degree when subjected to strong light, although they do not respond to mere differences of background. Although crustaceans cannot usually imitate the hues of the background on which they live except in a general fashion, this may often prove to be sufficient to render them inconspicuous enough to save them from being eaten.

When Is a Flea Not a Flea?

IF YOU SHOULD LIE ON A BEACH along the more seaward part of an estuary, your eyes may be drawn to small holes in the sand. These holes are only about as large as a matchstick would make and they seem to be quite empty; but that is because the animals which make them are nocturnal, and lie quietly deep down in their burrows when the sun is out. The tunnel occupants are small shrimps, with large circular eyes. They are known as beach fleas or sand fleas because of their jumping ability, although they are unrelated to real fleas.

The beach flea, *Talorchestia*, digs its burrows with great rapidity in moist sandy beaches above the high tide mark. In some areas this species and its relatives are so numerous that a dozen or more creatures can be found in almost any square inch of sand.

When *Talorchestia* emerges from its burrows after darkness falls, it becomes an active feeder on all types of decaying matter along the beach. Should you lie on the sand in the evening, you may be bothered by countless beach fleas creeping and jumping about you. It is quite easy to collect these little animals; they are attracted to light and a flashlight will cause many of them to gather in the pool of light cast by it.

A Busy Burrower—the Sand Bug

THE MOLE CRAB, *Emerita*, is another beach inhabitant common along the quiet shores of a bay. This too is a burrowing form, and a well-known one to thousands of beach-goers in the summer. It is a squat, molelike creature that lives in the sand precisely where the waves break. Its limbs are specialized digging organs, and the way in which it scuttles and burrows into the sand is responsible for its common name.

Mole crabs stay at the tide line and as the incoming tide pushes higher up the beach, they leave their shallow burrows and scurry up higher

Really a tiny shrimp with prominent eyes, the **beach flea** spends its life burrowing in the sand. During the day it lies hidden in its tunnel, coming out only at night to look for food in the decaying matter along the water's edge.

where they settle into the sand again. When the tide goes out they reverse the process. In any area where they are really abundant the waves will sometimes seem to be swarming with the small, active animals.

Their peculiar activity has good reason behind it; if you watch them carefully you will see that they settle in the sand at an angle and face the direction from which the waves come. Their bodies are hidden, but their long stalked eyes and bristled antennae extend upwards from the sand; in this way they are ready to capture their food by straining edible particles from the incoming water. They lead a precarious existence, since birds and fishes find them to be choice and easily dealt with morsels; furthermore, many human visitors to the beach seem to find irresistible the temptation to dig up a few to look at them more closely!

Emerita is worth close study, but this is carried out best in a shallow basin, where the animal can keep wet. Its streamlined covering protects most of the legs, and its weak and unprotected abdomen is doubled under the "chest" region. The powerful front digging legs can be seen in action if you place an inch of sand in the basin, and watch closely as the animal scoops out a burrow.

The Mantis Shrimp Is a Spiny Handful

THE BIZARRE MANTIS SHRIMP, *Chloridella,* is one animal not often seen except by fishermen aboard commercial trawlers, since it lives in fairly deep water in bays and the ocean, and burrows into the bottom. Only a net or a dredge which drags through the mud and sand is likely to bring one up; but when one is dredged up and thrown on deck, beware! It is covered with sharp spines and has two exceedingly sharp and powerful sickle-like claws that it will use without hesitation. These claws resemble in appearance and operation those of a praying mantis, hence the name. The animal grows to almost a foot in size, and most of this length is taken up with a large muscular abdomen. Although the

(top left)
The **mole crab,** or **sand bug,** often stays buried in the sand of a shoreline, with only its antennae and long stalked eyes extended into the shallow water. Its paddlelike legs can dig a burrow with surprising speed.

(top right)
Although its "saw" looks dangerous, the **sawfish** feeds mostly on small fishes and prefers to swim lazily in warm shallow coastal waters.

(above)
Caution should be used in handling the spine-covered **mantis shrimp.** If disturbed, it will strike out with its sharp, powerful claws, which it uses to capture prey and for defending its territory against intrusions by others of its kind.

mantis shrimp is supposed to be good eating, it has no commercial value because it is so difficult to collect.

The mantis shrimp is unusual in several respects. For one thing, its eyes are not borne on stalks as is the case with other shrimps, crabs and lobsters, but on a series of movable, ringlike segments. The eyes are not circular, but elliptical, and look somewhat like rounded croquet mallets. When buried in the bottom sand, only the oblong eyes and antennae extend above the surface, but under only a thin film of sand are the dangerous jackknife claws ready to whip out and catch any unwary animal that happens along. The mantis shrimp is not restricted to life on the bottom; nearly all shrimplike animals swim by means of their abdominal appendages, and in the mantis shrimp these appendages are exceedingly well developed and make the creature a powerful swimmer.

Chloridella is one animal to which the term "fierce" can justly be applied. Not only does it capture crabs, fishes, mollusks, sea anemones and worms, but it will not tolerate the presence of another of its own kind in the vicinity. If two are placed together in an aquarium, they attempt to creep up behind each other; and they will eventually fight until one of them is destroyed. Nor is this ferocity limited to the adult mantis shrimp; the small, glassy, free-swimming larva also has jointed claws, and will capture animals as large as itself. This larva is so transparent that in a plankton sample it seems to be no more than a pair of dark eyes, independent of a body. Perhaps this is an advantage in its constant hunt for food.

Hermit Crabs Have a Housing Problem

IF THE MANTIS SHRIMP is a "tiger", there are other animals that seem to be the clowns of the bay world—*Pagurus*, the hermit crab, for example. Of course amusement is only a human pastime, and the

(above)
Some fishes and shrimp are apparently immune to the poison of the anemone and can coexist with it. This **prawn** serves its anemone host by decoying fish so that they swim close enough to be caught and eaten.

(right)
Hermit crabs are not true crabs, despite their crablike claws. No hard outer shell protects their bodies, and they find shelter in discarded snail shells, dragging them around and retreating into them to hide from danger.

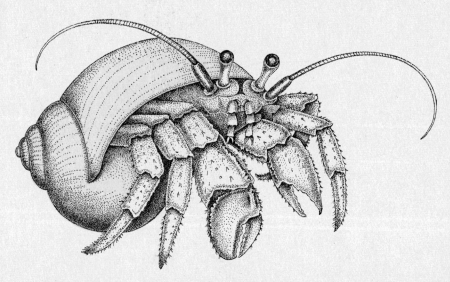

strange antics of hermit crabs are merely their means of getting along in the world, and highly successful ones, too.

Pagurus is not a true crab, although it does have crablike claws. Instead of a small abdomen tucked under a wide body, it has a large curved abdomen, quite vulnerable because there is no hard outer covering. The hermit crab defends itself by inserting its abdomen into a hollow object—usually a discarded snail shell. The shell is carried about and when danger threatens, the crab retreats into the shell and plugs up the opening with one of its claws. In some species the claw has evolved into a flat structure well suited for closing the aperture.

Most snail shells turn to the right, and hermit crab abdomens conform to this twist by also turning to the right. A crab which happens to find an unusual left-handed shell will adapt itself to make use of it—but will return to its normal "right-handed" twist once the shell is discarded. The tail appendages of the crab are specialized to hook on to the inside of the shell, and the hermit crab will allow itself to be pulled in two rather than let itself be withdrawn from the shell. The number of hermit crabs in almost any estuary could hardly be estimated. They are found in pools, behind sand bars, by breakwaters and anywhere that provides sheltered water.

Hermits rarely keep motionless for any length of time, but scavenge bits of decaying matter from the muddy bottom. Living on the outside of the snail shells are likely to be other animals that benefit by being taken about from place to place, although the transport is often somewhat rough! One kind of hydroid is especially adapted to living on the shells of hermits, and even has protective spines which keep it from being injured when the shell is dragged over the bottom.

Periodically a hermit crab has to search for a new shell, because after a time the one it currently occupies becomes an "uncomfortable fit". It will turn over any shell it comes across and probe to see if it already has an occupant. If it is empty, the hermit crab tries it on for size and if it fits, it is kept; if not, the crab quickly changes back to the old shell.

The housing problem is always acute for the hermit crab, and occasionally one may be seen dragging around an old can or small bottle. Of one thing you can be sure—there are few empty snail shells in bays; and more than a few aging snails have been "helped on their way" to provide a new house for an ambitious hermit.

One very large front claw (with the other of normal size) distinguishes the male **fiddler crab** from the female, which has two small front claws. The male feeds himself awkwardly with his giant claw, which apparently exists mostly for show and intimidation; he rarely engages in actual combat.

Salt Marshes Are Fiddler Crab Cities

I F WE GO UP THE BAY SHORE for several miles until the sandy beaches give way to mud flats and salt marshes, we enter the country of the fiddler crab, *Uca*. In marshes, fiddlers exist in numbers beyond belief —there are so many of them that their passage sounds like a rainstorm as they rush through the tall grass ahead of an intruder. Their burrows pit the mud banks for miles, and when conditions are quiet and undisturbed the entire area becomes alive with crawling, scuttling crabs. They are undemanding of their environment so long as the ground is soft enough for them to dig burrows and water is nearby. They appear to live equally well in salty, brackish or even nearly fresh water. Adult fiddlers cannot swim and only enter the water to moisten their gills. During high tides they remain in their flooded burrows holding a bubble of air for breathing.

One of the largest fiddler crabs can be recognized by the red spots on the male's large claw. This species builds burrows near the top of mud banks, and over the burrow opening it places an archway of mud pellets. Under this canopy the male fiddler rests, watching all that goes on outside. Smaller species of fiddlers, often associated with this larger form, build burrows straight into a mud bank with no porch roof.

The fiddler makes a burrow by scraping up mud which it forms into pellets, and carries them away by holding on with some of its legs while the others are used for walking. At the mouth of the burrow, the crab will hesitate and turn its erect, stalked eyes about looking for any sign of movement which might mean danger. If all is still the crab runs out, deposits its load of mud, pauses and looks about, runs back, pauses in the entrance and then ducks down out of sight. Several hundred crabs doing this simultaneously produce an effect which is both amusing and bewildering.

Female crabs have two small front claws of equal size, and this gives them an advantage when eating; for fiddlers scoop up bits of food in the mud and cram it into their mouths as fast as they can. The males are able to do this with only one claw—the price they pay for the huge claw that exists only to impress the females and frighten would-be antagonists. The large claw seems to be pure bluff, for although males do a lot of threatening, they seldom engage in combat.

During the winter, fiddler crabs hibernate deep within their burrows, but they emerge as soon as it grows warm again. In April the first eggs are laid. As with all crabs, the eggs are carried by the female beneath her tail, and she periodically goes down to the water to immerse them. When they hatch, the young are left in the water and swim away. These larvae do not look like crabs in the least: they are called *zoeae*.

The Odyssey of the Crab

ALL CRABS, FIDDLERS AND OTHERS, go through zoeal stages. The *zoea* is a small transparent creature with one or two long spines which give it buoyancy. As the zoea feeds and grows, it casts its outer skeleton periodically, each time becoming a little larger and a little more complex in structure. In the case of the edible blue crab which is described shortly, there are five zoeal stages. The first two swim as plankton at the surface, the third may be found at the surface or along the bottom, while the fourth and fifth stages exist only on the bottom.

Flattened, paddlelike hind legs propel a **swimming crab** through the water. Most other crabs have pointed hind legs, which are more suitable for running than for swimming.

The next moult results in a different form that resembles a shrimp. Early biologists thought this was an independent animal and named it *Megalops,* having no idea that it was another larval stage of a crab. The megalops stage is one in which advanced development is evident; it has large compound eyes, balancing organs at the base of the small antennae and numerous specialized appendages. In its next stage of development, the animal is clearly recognizable as a crab, with a broad body and small tail tucked up beneath the body.

The study of embryonic creatures such as these is a fascinating one because of the evidence it provides of the animal's evolutionary history. Almost all embryos pass through at least some stages during which they resemble more or less closely the equivalent embryos of ancestors now quite different—but which share with them a common genealogy. In most cases it is impossible to observe these developments in living creatures because they occur hidden from view—either inside the mother's body or else within the opaque egg-case. Not so with the water-living crustaceans. The crab, as just described, goes through a number of completely different stages before it becomes an adult. It is true that two of these occur within the egg, but the others closely resemble more primitive free-swimming shrimp-forms that exist in profusion in the oceans today. Thus in one animal there is evidence of a history of a long and complex evolutionary process. These larval and embryonic stages in animals and plants take a great deal of the guesswork out of our attempts to reconstruct the past history of living things.

Crustacean eyes are worth studying closely; and those of a crab are easy to see because they are comparatively large. As with insect eyes, they are made up of many individual fixed-focus eyes, each of which forms a simple image in a separate direction. The images formed by such eyes probably result in a series of crude pictures, each slightly different from the next. In certain crustaceans dark shutter-like cells slide up and down to regulate the amount of light entering each individual eye. When an image falls across a few of these eyes it probably means nothing to the animal, but as more eyes pick up the shadow, outside motion is indicated and the animal responds by moving away if the image is large (and therefore dangerous) or perhaps toward it if it is small (and indicates food).

A Million-dollar Crab

ONE OF THE LARGEST CRUSTACEANS common to Atlantic bays, the blue crab, *Callinectes,* is of considerable commercial importance in the United States. Although it can often be found along the open sea coast it is far more numerous in the brackish water of estuaries—even in those which are sometimes nearly fresh due to the overflow of river water.

The adult blue crab has bright blue and red markings on its claws

Not yet recognizable as a crab, the early larval **zoea** looks like a different creature entirely. As it grows, finding food near the water's surface, it periodically discards its outer skeleton and gradually develops into a full-grown crab.

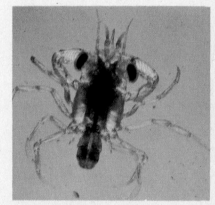

Advanced development of the larval crab is seen in the **megalops** stage, in which most of the organs and appendages of the mature crab have been formed. Note especially the large eyes.

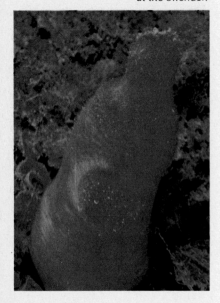

An unsavory-looking mass of red, rather shapeless "sea pork" is really a living colony of primitive **sea squirts.** When disturbed, the whole mass contracts, squirting out a jet of water at the offender.

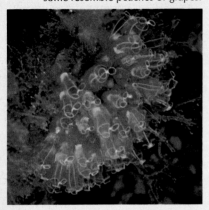

Sea squirts, or **tunicates,** are found in a wide variety of forms and colors. Some are solid masses, some are translucent or a golden yellow, and some resemble peaches or grapes.

and back. This animal is typical of the swimming crabs in having rear legs which serve as efficient paddles; it does not use its abdomen and abdominal appendages in propulsion as shrimps do. The abdominal segments which are so important in the shrimp have become much reduced in size in the crabs; the abdomen is a mere vestige, folded underneath the body, and is used for little else than attachment of eggs and as a digestive tube.

Next to its bright markings, the most impressive items of the adult blue crab are the front legs that have developed into sharp, powerful claws which the crab uses with speed and skill. It takes some experience to pick up an active blue crab without painful nips and cuts.

Females carrying eggs appear in the spring, reach their greatest numbers in midsummer, and continue to be present until summer is past. An egg-bearing female is called a "sponge crab", due to the appearance of the large yellowish egg mass carried under the tail. The eggs are very small, and there may be as many as five million in one mass. After the embryos have developed the eggs hatch and larvae emerge. Hatching occurs quite soon after fertilization, and is followed by the transitional stages of development already described.

By the onset of their first winter the animals are no longer planktonic larvae, but are recognizably the crabs they will be for the rest of their lives. Shedding of the "shell" occurs periodically, with the crabs clinging to some firm stationary object to assist the process. Directly after moulting, crabs have an increased market value as "soft-shelled" crabs that can be cooked and eaten in their entirety. Hard crabs have to be cracked open and the meat picked out.

After three to four years of growing, blue crabs are mature, and reproduce after the female has moulted for the last time. Full-grown blue crabs will measure six inches across the back and should be treated with the utmost respect! When a crab cannot escape, it faces its attacker with claws held wide and open. If your hand is within striking range, both claws will stab out together and even if the pincers don't grab hold, you still can receive a painful wound where the sharp claw tips have punctured the skin. If crabs are held from above near the joint between the tail and broad back, their claws cannot reach you; but watch somebody with the necessary skill do it before you try it yourself!

Our Lowly Relatives

SEA PORK" WOULD NOT MEAN MUCH to a seaside visitor, nor would the sight of a reddish, sand-covered mass. But the mass, actually a colony of sea squirts, might create an uncomfortable feeling in this same visitor were he to realize that sea squirts, or tunicates, are members of man's own major group, the chordates.

Simple tunicates live separately; but *Amaroucium*, the sea pork, has so evolved that it lives in a packed "colony". Each colony originates

(left)
The **common mackerel,** one the many ocean fish found in bays, is a voracious feeder and a graceful swimmer. Blue-green and silvery, with distinctive dark ripple markings on its back, it can be seen darting in the waters along the northeastern coast of North America and western coast of Europe.

(below)
Shorebirds such as the **plover** feed on fish and small animals found in the waters along the coast. With its alert, yellow-rimmed eyes, the plover can spot tiny animals in waters only an inch or two deep, where it doesn't have to compete for food with predatory fish.

from a single parent, and with successive budding results in a large cluster of strangely degenerate animals. The "social relationship" is of a low order once they have budded; they feed independently, and in competition with one another, from the surrounding water. They reproduce periodically, releasing into the water tiny tadpole-like larvae which swim off and, if they escape being eaten, eventually attach themselves to the bottom and grow into a new colony.

While digging in a sand flat for clams, you may notice small burrows with coils of sand castings about the entrance; and if you uncover the animals that construct the burrows you will find them to be sluggish, yellow-and-orange acorn worms that seem hardly worth a second glance. But these acorn worms also are chordates, and therefore members of man's family tree.

An acorn worm is simpler in structure than an earthworm, but it is the pattern of the structure that makes it significant. It has all the basic requirements for the development of nervous, respiratory, circulatory and digestive systems, and it is probably not very different from the remote ancestors of the great variety of vertebrate animals.

Bays Are Gathering Places for Ocean Fishes

A BAY IS A GREAT SPAWNING AND FEEDING BASIN for all types of fishes. The skates, rays and small sharks abound; the representatives of those families which do not have bony skeletons. Most of them feed on the bottom, where they find vast quantities of worms, mollusks and shrimps to eat. The variety of true, bony fishes in bays and estuaries is almost endless, and the population of any one species is likely to be enormous. Plankton feeders such as menhaden can sometimes be seen feeding at the surface for miles in all directions; sea "trout" and croakers feed along the bottom in large schools. If you are in a small boat at night, and listen carefully through the hull, you may hear grunts and croaks from schools of croakers as they pass beneath.

(top left)
The handsome **red mullet,** often found with vivid golden stripes along its flanks, prefers to stay close to shore and around coral reefs. It feeds on the worms and shrimps of shallow waters, using the whiskerlike **barbels** under its chin for touching and tasting.

(top right)
Large numbers of silvery **smelts** inhabit waters close to the shores of estuaries. Full-grown at only eight inches, they are small but forbidding with their large jaws—the lower jutting beyond the upper—and their rows of fine, thin teeth.

A common bay fish, the common silverside, *Menidia,* is seen frequently in large schools along the water's edge. It has a conspicuous silvery stripe down its side, and when the sunlight catches these bands on hundreds of individuals the water sparkles and shines with light. *Menidia* probably never migrate to the open seas, but spend their entire existence over shallow sandy bottoms where they eat small crustaceans, mollusks, fish eggs, algae and insects that fall into the water. They spawn in such great numbers that the quantity of eggs may thicken the water in shallow marshy areas.

Silversides spend their summers within a few yards of the water line, and follow the tide in and out. In winter they leave the shallow areas and descend to depths of over a hundred feet to escape the chill of the surface waters. They may be caught with seines when close to shore, and in some areas they are caught and sold as bait for bluefish, mackerel and striped bass. Fried in quantity and served on tables as "whitebait", they make delicious eating.

It was mentioned earlier that bays occasionally attract southern, warm-water animals from the Gulf Stream. In the summer, animals going north in the stream find themselves becoming chilled. A bay, warmed by the sun, provides water temperatures more closely resembling the conditions to which they are accustomed and they head in to shore. During the years that biologists have studied estuaries, they have come to realize that almost anything that swims can appear in a typical bay.

The Ocean Has Its Porcupines

PORCUPINEFISH, ALSO CALLED BURRFISH or spiny boxfish, is really a creature of the south, but has been found in the far north. One of the puffers, a true ocean fish, it is more common in offshore waters and is not characteristic of bays. It is mentioned here to remind us that bays may harbor many ocean wanderers.

The porcupinefish is a rigid fish, armed with large, triangular spines. The body cannot be bent, and the only visible moving parts are the rapidly fluttering fins; it has no scales, and its teeth are fused together to form sharp, cutting beaks. When the fish is irritated, it can inflate itself with water—or air if it is pulled out of water. This trick probably serves to discourage any predator from swallowing it—it would be just as easy to swallow a horse chestnut!

The common croaker, *Micropogon undulatus,* is a well-known inhabitant of shallow coastal waters, and is eagerly sought by those who enjoy fishing as a sport. This fish shares with most of its close relatives the curious ability to produce sound by strumming a special muscle against its swim bladder. The noises thus produced are loud enough to be heard from the decks of boats, and the sound is almost deafening under water. A school of croakers swimming close to the hull of a boat is enough to keep the crew awake, and more than one skipper has on occasion been alarmed by the noise into thinking something is wrong with his vessel. Some fishermen send a crew member below decks to "listen in" and direct the helmsman to the area where the sound is loudest.

Bays are feeding and spawning grounds for croakers, although their complete life history is still unknown. The fishes begin appearing in bay waters during March and April, remain until September and October, and then disappear from the cooling coastal regions for regions unknown somewhere in the deeper ocean.

The migratory routes of many fishes are still mysteries to biologists, although continuous work by research teams at university and state

Most of the time **grunion** are very hard to spot. Spending their lives at sea, they come to shore only to spawn at the high-tide line when the moon is full or new. Then they surface by the millions, only to return shortly to the sea once again.

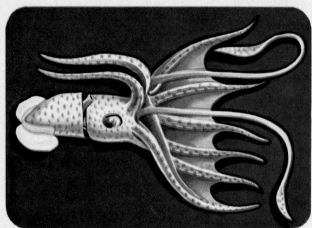

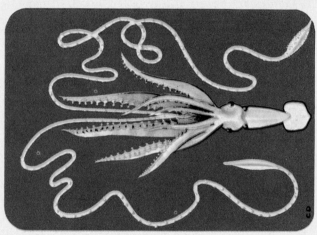

(top left)
Inhabitants of temperate and colder waters, **herrings** swim in tight schools, almost always near the surface. They search constantly for plankton, straining many mouthfuls of water through their small, feeble teeth.

(top right)
Estuaries may shelter any number of unusual marine animals, such as the **squid,** a creature with ten tentacles and a slender cylindrical body.

(above, left)
This fanciful-looking squid has six of its tentacles joined by a pink membranous web. It moves in the water like a jellyfish.

(above, right)
A squid has eight arms, which are similar to those of an octopus, and two longer tentacles. The long tentacles in this species are several times the length of the body.

laboratories is narrowing the gaps in knowledge of many of the economically important fishes. For example, a widespread investigation is being carried on concerning the menhaden—a fish of great commercial importance because of the variety of fish products derived from it. The importance of bays during the early life of this fish cannot be overestimated. Apparently the success of the whole species depends upon how well they fare in coastal bays and estuaries.

The Bay—a World in Itself

ONE OF THE GREATEST DIFFERENCES between the estuary environment and that of the open shoreline is the absence of rough surf. The former is commonly the home of much life along the shore and in the sand at the water's edge. Along the ocean shore this same life may be nearly absent, since it is incapable of withstanding the frequent pounding of the heavy surf.

Animals existing in mud usually are found feeding on decaying organic matter, while those of sandy bottoms are more likely to be predators. The greatest abundance and variety of animals seems to lie in the area where the sand is mixed with sediment.

Bay animals often are adapted to withstand the changeable conditions of estuaries. If they live between the levels of high and low tide, they must remain moist in some fashion while they are exposed to air. They may have shells that close, or tubes which can be plugged, while others retreat into deep burrows. Animals living along the bottom of the bay may use similar methods of withstanding sudden alterations of temperature or chemical nature of the water. Swimming animals can move from one area to another for feeding and breeding, and so are able to choose a new suitable location when their old environment undergoes a change. But animals that spend their lives attached to the bottom must either be able to tolerate such changes as occur, or die.

In any estuary there are frequent physical and chemical changes in the water—and also fluctuations in its animal populations. Fishes and other swimming marine forms have free access to bay waters where they may remain for long periods—or where they perhaps intrude only briefly before continuing their journeys along the coast. Those species that drift with currents or crawl on the bottom migrate in and out of bays in patterns which no one as yet really understands. So little has been done, and so much needs to be learned about estuaries, that they are highly profitable fields for further studies.

Research currently being carried on indicates that bays, estuaries and water from salt water marshes may provide the bulk of the basic nourishment for most of the animals in the seas. Big fishes feed on little ones, and the smallest marine animals feed directly upon the microscopic plants that grow in shallow bays and sounds. There may come a time in the not too distant future when men will be trained as marine farmers to harvest the great crop that grows luxuriantly in our coastal waters.

► *The astoundingly beautiful plants and animals that live on these magnificent structures in the sea.*

Life on a Coral Reef

THE SEA IS a sheltered place in which to live. All things necessary for an animal's living and welfare are present in abundance, and drastic weather changes such as we experience on dry land are unknown. Three-quarters of the surface waters vary in temperature only five degrees or less throughout the whole year.

Marine creatures are surrounded by the compound essential for all life—water. It surrounds them with dissolved oxygen and carbon dioxide and ample supplies of the minerals and salts which an animal must have in order to live. One of these dissolved materials, calcium carbonate, is extracted from the water by individual coral animals and used to form the coral's "skeleton". Surface waters of the seas also contain immense quantities of plankton, or miscroscopic plants and animals. The word "plankton" comes from the Greek word "planktos" and means wandering—an appropriate name for drifting forms. As on the land surface of the earth, plants are the start of the food chain of living creatures in the water. The animal kingdom depends completely upon the plant kingdom.

Minute one-celled plants, called diatoms, are present in the ocean in astronomical numbers. They may double their numbers every second day, and yield many tons per acre in a year. They compose six-tenths of plankton and are eaten by single-celled animals called protozoa. The protozoa are eaten by slightly larger forms, copepods, and so it goes.

Underwater exploration seldom yields such beautiful and informative sights as when it is carried on around a coral reef. Not only is each reef a well-adapted ecological system, but plant and animal life may be found there in almost limitless variety. For example, among the colorful corals one may happen to stumble upon an **octopus' cavern** (photo, top right).

For example, one hundred thousand pounds of diatoms will produce 10,000 pounds of copepods, which can be converted into 1,000 pounds of herring or smelt; these fish, in turn, will yield 100 pounds of mackerel, and the mackerel will make ten pounds of tuna. Finally, when a growing human eats ten pounds of tuna he will build about one pound of human flesh. Roughly nine-tenths of the food intake of a growing animal is used to produce muscular and glandular energy.

Since ocean dwellers are free of the relentless force of gravity, they have no need for heavy supporting limbs or strong skeletal structures. The bodies of fishes have developed streamlining which allows them to pass through a medium six hundred times as dense as air. Their bones and limbs have been developed for digging, fighting, catching prey and swimming, rather than for support. Whereas a six-ton elephant is our largest land creature, whales reach a weight of one hundred and fifty tons. Perfectly adapted for an oceanic life, they are quickly suffocated on land, since they cannot raise their own vast weight to draw air into their lungs.

The variety of marine life is amazing. There are some ninety thousand named species of invertebrates, or animals without backbones, and biologists tell us that at least another ninety thousand have yet to be classified. About twenty-five thousand species of true fishes roam the seas.

The Reef-builders

BENEATH THE SURFACE of the oceans in tropical latitudes there exists a region that is like no other on earth—the coral reef. The reef is created by minute animals, the corals, which secrete calcium carbonate to form external "skeletons". These are really like tiny rock-hard houses that protect the coral polyps. When the polyps die, the next generation builds *its* houses on top of the empty ones. After thousands of years, the colonies of polyps have built a huge structure, which we call a coral reef.

Reef-building corals are found in many parts of the world, but are

(bottom left)
A one-celled animal like the **amoeba** reproduces itself through **fission,** or cell division. First the nucleus divides, and then the body separates into two parts, each a new animal with its own nucleus.

(bottom right)
A large and mostly marine group of protozoans, **foraminifers** concentrate calcium or silica, with which they form a protective and often intricate shell about their bodies. The shell is perforated with many tiny holes through which slender strands of protoplasm can be protruded.

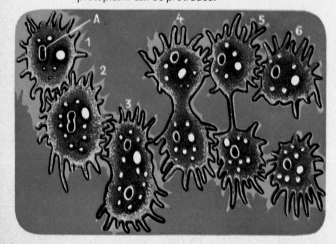

only common in a belt along the equator, running roughly from thirty degrees north latitude to thirty degrees south. The first conclusion we draw from this fact is that reef-building corals flourish only in warm waters; and such is exactly the case. The most rapid growth and the greatest number of species both occur where surface waters range from 77° to 84° F. (25° to 29° C.). The reef-builders will grow in waters that average 70° F. (21° C.) or warmer, but if the temperature drops more than a few degrees below this point, or remains lower for very long, the corals cannot survive and reefs are not formed.

Corals also require light in order to thrive. This is due to the fact that their body tissues contain *algae* and *zooxanthellae*, tiny plants which absorb sunlight and produce food. For this reason, coral reefs are only formed at shallow depths, where sunlight can penetrate clear waters; the corals grow vigorously down to about sixty-five feet, and thin out as depth increases. Sometimes minute plants give the corals their hue, which fades to white when the coral is taken out of water. "Precious" coral has a permanent tint from minerals in the water.

For many years scientists believed that the contained algae were absolutely necessary for the coral's survival; recent studies, however, dispute this point. It is now thought that the contained algae produce food which is absorbed directly by the coral polyp and which helps the coral to grow faster, bigger and healthier. It has been proved that corals will stay alive in total darkness indefinitely. It is interesting to note that under these conditions, and when a coral is starved, the algae are not digested by the polyp, but are ejected. A great deal remains to be learned, but it appears that when conditions are beneficial for the plant-animal relationships (of alga and polyp), the corals are strong, vigorous, healthy, grow rapidly—and form reefs. However, some corals, even reef-builders, apparently gain no benefits from contained algae. These corals are found in dark places, such as the floors of Scandinavian fjords, and ocean bottoms at the astounding depth of twenty-four thousand feet.

Corals do best when bathed in an adequate supply of fresh ocean water. The most vigorous growth occurs on the seaward or windward

(bottom left)
All life in the ocean is interrelated. At the base of the food chain are one-celled plants and animals, which are eaten by slightly larger creatures, like copepods. These in turn are eaten by still larger animals, such as this **shad,** which may itself be food for some larger or fiercer predator.

(bottom right)
Well-known to most of us, the **tuna** is a popular fish for human consumption. Although there are many sizes of tuna, fishermen have been known to catch specimens as much as ten feet long.

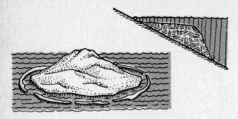

FRINGING REEF

BARRIER REEF

SUNKEN ISLAND

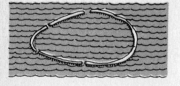

ATOLL

Every coral reef belongs to one of three main categories and is described in relationship to a body of land. Stationary or gradually rising shorelines may be surrounded by a **fringing reef,** which often extends outward for some distance. Where coasts are slowly sinking, **barrier reefs** may be formed, separated from the land by a deep lagoon and growing upward just fast enough to stay within reach of the sun's penetrating rays. If an island has sunk completely below sea level, it can leave a circular barrier reef called an **atoll.**

sides of islands, cays and atolls; the more exposed the area, the better the corals seem to grow. It is interesting to note that corals are seldom found where fresh-water rivers empty into the sea. In the past, men believed, logically, that fresh water killed the corals. It now appears that the silt and sediment carried by the rivers do the killing, since corals supported above the bottom grow successfully in these same areas.

There are still a great many things that man does not know about corals and the reasons for their growth. Over a hundred years ago Charles Darwin wondered why coral reefs grow beautifully and reach the surface in one place, while a few miles away, under apparently identical conditions, the same species only forms submerged reefs. We still do not know the answers to many of the questions Darwin raised so long ago, but some of his theories are borne out by modern research. As an example, Darwin theorized that an atoll was formed by a slowly sinking volcanic cone, surrounded by a fringing reef of coral. He wrote that the coral grew upward as fast as the mountain sank downward, and that if one drilled deep enough into an atoll, he would find volcanic rock. This was done at Eniwetok Atoll, and volcanic rock *was* found—at 4,220 feet below the surface!

So we see that corals need warm waters, clear enough for sunlight to penetrate and clean enough to contain adequate food in the form of healthy plants and animals forming the plankton common to open-ocean surface waters. There must also be shallow banks or shore lines for the corals to grow upon. If we examine the world-wide distribution of reef-building corals, we notice that they are largely absent from the western side of continents and large islands. This is explained by the sea currents produced by the earth's rotation, which tend to bring cold deep waters to the surface; they are too cold for corals to tolerate.

We also notice that there are more coral reef areas north of the equator than south, even within the belt from thirty degrees north latitude to thirty degrees south; cool surface waters or some other unsuitable condition below the equator are the cause. The island of Bermuda is one major coral area well north of the thirtieth parallel. Reef-building corals can thrive here because the Gulf Stream brings warm Caribbean water into the area, making it in effect a tropical sea regardless of its location—a fact much appreciated by winter visitors from the northern United States and Europe.

The most prolific, densely populated communities of animals anywhere in the world, above water or below, are the Indo-Pacific coral reefs. Conditions here are better for coral growth than anywhere else, and both the size of the corals and the number of species are unequalled. The coral reef is certainly one of the most beautiful and best adapted ecological systems extant, and, unless vastly changed by man's tampering, its inhabitants survive and thrive today as they have for many centuries.

Banks of Coral

CORALS WILL GROW anywhere under suitable conditions. When these conditions are met over a large area of sea bottom, corals are found in enormous banks instead of in fringing or barrier reefs, or atolls. Banks occur in the southern Atlantic, especially amid and between the Bahama Islands. These Bahama Banks cover hundreds of square miles and are an ideal place to study shallow-water marine life. The depth of water on the banks themselves is usually thirty feet or less, while adjacent channels may be thousands of feet deep. Both shallow-water and deep-water forms may be found within a short distance of each other. So extensive are the Bahama Banks that sailors crossing them are out of sight of land in all directions—except straight down, where the bottom slides by under ten or fifteen feet of crystal-clear water. It's an eerie and unnerving sensation at first, especially to sailors from northern waters, where if you can see bottom you're already aground!

Corals are one of the major building materials of the world. The largest edifice ever created by living creatures is the Great Barrier Reef of Australia, stretching 1,260 miles and covering eighty thousand square miles. Picture a coral bank up to five hundred feet high—almost half as high as the Empire State Building—with one end in Canada and the other end in Cuba. Visualize also, if you will, what the Pacific might look like if the water were drained away and we could see the coral atolls and plateaux that break or nearly reach the surface. These rise from ocean bottoms as much as 35,000 feet deep, and if the Eniwetok borings are typical, the coral can be almost a mile thick over the underlying rock. The mighty creations of man seem small indeed compared to what these tiny animals have built.

The reefs form an incomparable breeding place for myriads of fish,

A typical **fringing reef** is made up of several sections. The seaward region (left) contains almost all of the living coral, which grows fastest here. As a result, this area is nearest the surface. The sand-bottomed **lagoon** (middle) is a sheltered stretch of warm waters, from a hundred yards to several miles wide, where plant and animal life flourish. At the shoreline, the sand beach slopes gently upward to join with dry land (right), which is covered with permanent vegetation.

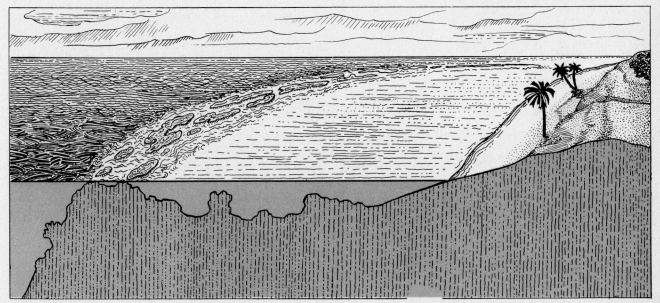

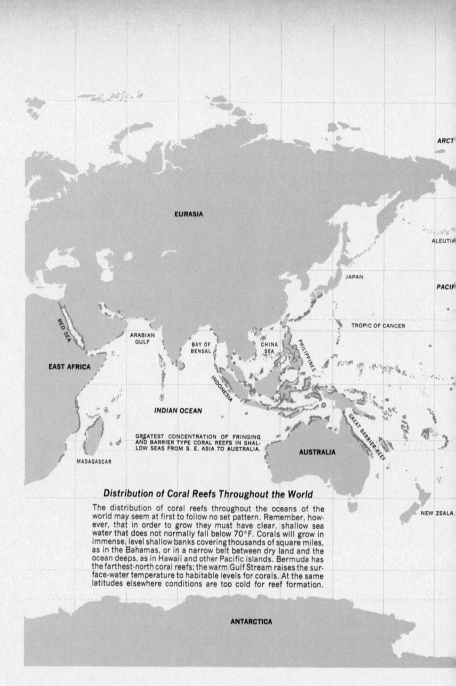

ARCT

ALEUTIA

JAPAN

PACIF

TROPIC OF CANCER

EURASIA

RED SEA

ARABIAN GULF

BAY OF BENGAL

CHINA SEA

PHILIPPINES

EAST AFRICA

INDONESIA

GREAT BARRIER REEF

INDIAN OCEAN

GREATEST CONCENTRATION OF FRINGING AND BARRIER TYPE CORAL REEFS IN SHALLOW SEAS FROM S. E. ASIA TO AUSTRALIA.

AUSTRALIA

MADAGASCAR

NEW ZEALA

Distribution of Coral Reefs Throughout the World

The distribution of coral reefs throughout the oceans of the world may seem at first to follow no set pattern. Remember, however, that in order to grow they must have clear, shallow sea water that does not normally fall below 70°F. Corals will grow in immense, level shallow banks covering thousands of square miles, as in the Bahamas, or in a narrow belt between dry land and the ocean deeps, as in Hawaii and other Pacific islands. Bermuda has the farthest-north coral reefs; the warm Gulf Stream raises the surface-water temperature to habitable levels for corals. At the same latitudes elsewhere conditions are too cold for reef formation.

ANTARCTICA

A coral reef provides small fish with protection from larger sea animals as well as from man. Cavities in a large reef may shelter thousands of fish, including the boldly striped **sergeant-major,** an expert at retreating.

crabs, eels and shellfish. Without reefs there would be little refuge for the young of many species and few of them would live to maturity. A coral reef is a well balanced community. Hundreds of forms flourish and grow with no one of them in danger of extinction or overcrowding. Except for small areas where men have overfished a certain species, the carnivorous animals, the vegetarian animals and the plants stay in their proper ratio. In fresh-water lakes this balance is often upset by man's effort to "improve" things without fully investigating the situation. Results are often disastrous to the wildlife community.

Jellyfish, individual hydroids, anemones and coral animals without

Needle-sharp spines, which can cause painful wounds, make the **sea urchin** an animal to avoid. It is well to be on the lookout for it near its favorite places: coral rocks and sandy ocean floors.

their limestone skeletons all look somewhat alike and in fact belong to the same family, the coelenterates. The name, which means "hollow gut", stems from the fact that the body of such animals is one large digestive cavity. All coelenterates are carnivorous. A circle of tentacles surrounds the mouth; with these tentacles the animal snares its prey and passes it to the central mouth. Though the reef-building corals are restricted to warm, shallow waters, coelenterates are found in great abundance in temperate and cold zones and in the cold and eternally dark ocean abysses, many thousands of feet below the surface.

There is apparently a great deal of variation in the rate of growth of corals, even among members of the same species. Some of the reasons for this are known; many are not. The fastest-growing species observed, in the East Indies, seem to grow upward about four inches in a year. The red coral of the Mediterranean Sea is harvested for ornaments about every ten years, and it has grown about a foot in that time. There have been cases where channels were dug for the passage of copra schooners, and coral growth has made them impassable within ten years.

In many parts of the Pacific any chart more than twenty years old is considered worthless, since the coral growth in that time would have made significant changes in the water depths. It is not wise to trust a channel marked "safe" on the chart unless personal soundings prove it so. Even today, many parts of the Caribbean Sea have not been accurately charted in over a hundred years, since a voyage by a British research vessel in the early part of the nineteenth century. There are many places where the underwater features have not changed significantly, and it is still safe to navigate by the charts; but in other areas the author has found (by bouncing a seventy-foot yawl on the bottom with a loud crunch) that channels have shoaled considerably, and in a number of cases are not now to be found at their indicated locations. It is surprising to realize that as little as ten or twenty years can make so much difference, as corals have lived in the sea for well over four hundred million years.

After all this time, we really know very little about corals, and there are only a handful of men who can be classed as experts in this field. Since the growth of coral affects commerce and shipping operations, it is possible that research in this field will be given more attention (and money) than might be the case if it were simply of pure scientific interest.

Aside from its effects on the shipping waterways of the world, coral has little commercial value. There are small industries in the Mediterranean, Japan, the Pescadores and Formosa concerned with the manufacture of ornaments and beads from "precious coral", or *Corallium*. This branching coral, with its familiar red or pink, is the best-known coral, widely used in the making of jewelry. The industry has been carried on since ancient times, the coral being harvested by dragging clumsy wooden crosses behind boats and catching the broken-off coral in nets. Since this procedure destroys perhaps four times as much coral as it brings to the surface, it is little wonder that precious coral is found today only in protected caves and recesses the draggers cannot reach. Because of the difficulties of harvesting it, red coral has attained considerable value in the past, and has been traded for pearls, emeralds and rubies, and used to decorate the shields of Celts in Great Britain before the Roman conquest. Like many rare or valuable items, precious coral has been believed to have magical qualities (hence its appearance on war shields) and therapeutic values.

The soft, expanded look of this **gorgonian coral** is a result of the individual polyps reaching out with their tentacles to catch bits of food in the water. This is a rare sight during daylight hours, since most corals feed only at night.

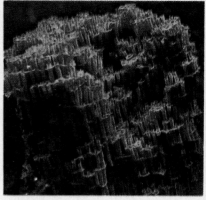

(top left)
Even though it is a fast grower, the **stag-horn coral** is extremely delicate and cannot stand up against storms or even the constant pounding of waves.

(top center)
Vibrantly colored corals usually owe their hues to millions of microscopic algae that live in the tissues of the polyps or within the coral skeleton. However, the deep blues of some corals may be caused by the presence of iron salts or by some other factor. This **clubbed-finger coral** is the only common blue coral in the Atlantic.

(top right)
Striking clusters of tubular shapes are formed by the **organ-pipe coral.** Each "pipe" houses a single polyp, which moves upward as the tube gets higher. It thus abandons the lower part of the tube, which may become the home of a worm, crab or other animal.

The Many Forms of Coral

CORALS TAKE MANY different forms, and appear in just about every shape one could imagine. The many-branched stag-horn coral is typical of the fragile forms usually found behind the seaward "break-water" of more massive types. Though it is easily broken by wave action, it seems to grow rather rapidly and must be classed as an important reef-builder. The palmated corals commonly called "antler" or "moose-horn" are more sturdy and better able to resist breakage. However the prize for durability must go to the brain and stone corals, which grow in a rounded lump that may reach several feet across. These corals, offering a minimum of surface per pound of weight, can resist the wildest storms (or almost the wildest, at any rate). They are much different from branching corals in surface appearance, besides being of a different shape; these massive corals have grooves, instead of pits or cavities, in their surfaces. The grooves contain the animals, as might be supposed, but in this case the animals are joined to form one long groove-shaped group of polyps, with the tentacles along both sides of the groove and a row of mouths stretching along the bottom of each groove. Whether or not this is as effective an arrangement for feeding as the branching corals where each polyp lives in an individual cup, the overall form of a brain coral is certainly stronger and more resistant to breakage from wave action.

It is not surprising, then, to find the rounded corals predominating on the outer edges of Atlantic reefs at depths of thirty to sixty feet and deeper. Behind this barrier of massive rounded corals we find a gradually sloping region where the branching corals are protected enough to thrive at average depths of ten to thirty feet; a wide variety of corals and other marine invertebrates are found in this region. Further shoreward is a sloping shoal where small corals, sea fans and other soft corals, and masses of fire-coral are found; this shoal extends to the beach itself.

Corals occur in a lot of different hues, ranging from reds through yellows and browns to greens, blues and violets; practically no tone is missing altogether. The tint is usually produced by the plants (algae) that live in the tissues of the polyps, and the algae that grow within the porous lime skeleton. By far the most common hue is yellow-brown in various shades; there is probably an excellent reason why these corals are healthier or safer than others, but this is one of the many questions for which we do not yet have an answer. There is a very pretty blue coral in Indo-Pacific waters (*Heliopora*) whose hue may be due to iron salts; the only common blue coral in the Atlantic is the clubbed-finger coral. These bright corals are occasionally collected for souvenirs by tourists, who are subsequently disappointed to find that the coral skeletons are pure white when removed from the sea and dried out.

The organ-pipe coral is an intriguing one, both in hue and form. The skeleton is red, even after drying. The polyps of a living specimen are a beautiful emerald-green, making a striking contrast against the red tubes of the skeleton. This is not as rugged as a completely solid skeleton, but the organ-pipe is an important reef-building species in some areas. Each vertical tube contains one individual polyp, which occupies the top portion of the tube, moving upward as the skeleton grows. The crosswise connectors serve not only as strengthening members, but contain the endodermal or digestive canals.

Some Corals Can Bend

NOT ALL CORAL animals form the stony limestone skeletons of the reef-builders. Some are quite flexible and sway back and forth in the ocean currents. This group is called the gorgonian corals and includes many forms. The common names of sea fans, sea whips, sea rods and sea plumes give a good idea of the appearance of the gorgonians. They are tough and leathery and are very often dried for use as decorations.

Most familiar of these is the graceful sea fan, one of the most common and spectacular facets of undersea landscape of the tropical Atlantic. It is hard to realize that this fan is a colony of living animals which catch and eat other small animals and plants. A close examination of a sea fan, however, will reveal the coral animals, or polyps, that secrete the substance of which the fan is constructed. These polyps appear as little dark dots when they have retreated to the cavities in which they live. When the polyps extend their tentacles into the water, the coral assumes a somewhat feathery appearance and we say it is "expanded".

Since sea fans are strongly sensitive to light, divers very seldom see them expanded. Almost all corals retract during the day (or when disturbed) and become expanded only at night, when they feed on plankton, organic detritus and the like. Sea fans do retain much of their hue when dried, and are widely used as decorations and souvenir items.

Belonging to the gorgonian corals, the **sea fan** seems like a miracle of delicacy and color. The beautiful "fan" is produced by secretions of the polyps that inhabit this gently swaying coral.

Fortunately, they are common and obviously have a good reproductive ratio; despite widespread predations, they are still plentiful. Sea fans and other gorgonians form the bulk of the "sea gardens" shown to tourists in glass-bottom boats and to neophyte skin divers. The delicacy of form and hue exists nowhere else on earth and never seems to lose its fascination, even for the experienced diver. The sea fans and other gorgonians, the organ-pipe coral and the precious coral are all *alcyonarians,* a group of invertebrates with eight tentacles instead of six.

Beautiful but Poisonous

A SEA ANEMONE adds a bright note, looking for all the world like some sort of flower. There is good reason for its alluring appearance: it attracts small fish and, when they come close to investigate, paralyzes them with its tentacles and devours them. The tentacles are equipped with stinging cells, or nematocysts. These are tiny hypodermic needles that inject a poison. The sting of a jellyfish and the "burning" sensation produced by fire-coral are caused by nematocysts. These specialized cells are very effective for capturing small prey, but there is a mystery surrounding them. Apparently some fish are immune to their poison, or in an unexplained manner are able to avoid being stung. Clownfishes and some others actually dive into an anemone when danger approaches, hiding deep down amid the tentacles. They may possibly help the anemone slightly by decoying fish into range, but the relationship is not well understood. The Portuguese man-of-war jellyfish, also armed with nematocysts, shelters a small fish in similar manner; the fish is apparently completely immune, and spends most of its life in among the tentacles. The nematocysts of both the man-of-war and of anemones are known to have killed humans on occasion.

Anemones are capable of a creeping or gliding motion, but spend most of their time in one place. The top speed, when in motion, is three to four inches an hour! There are many forms of anemones that spend their lives burrowing in the mud, either feeding on animals they find there or coming to the surface and spreading their bright-hued tentacles.

The common southern Atlantic anemone has whitish tentacles tipped with a spot of blue, purple or lavender. It is seldom more than eight or nine inches across. One species found in Australian waters measures three feet across the body alone, but this is an exceptional case. Experiments have shown that the size of an anemone is directly related to the amount of food available. It is possible to increase or decrease the size of a specimen at will, by over- or underfeeding the animal.

Anemones are very well adapted to their way of life. Specimens have been kept for eighty years in laboratory tanks; their life spans may reach three hundred years. Single individuals have been observed to occupy the same crevice on a reef for thirty years. Their only enemies seem to be certain fish which nibble off tentacles. These losses are soon replaced by healthy new growth.

Anemones reproduce in one of three ways. They may simply split, forming two individuals, or they may produce eggs that grow into free-swimming larvae. Finally, as an anemone slides about, pieces of the base are left behind to grow into complete animals. Occasionally a complete circle of pieces will sometimes be left, producing as many as twelve tiny new anemones.

Camouflage is effected by withdrawing the tentacles until the animal resembles a blob of jelly. Predators are not attracted and exposure to the air at low tide causes no harm.

They Walk with Their Arms

STARFISH ARE FAMILIAR to people all over the world. Many have found their way inland after having been dried out for use as ornamental souvenirs. Sometimes they are gaudily painted, but this seems unnecessary in view of the rich reds, browns, yellows and purples of the natural animal. Most tropical starfish are larger than the northern forms and have broader arms. Starfish usually have five arms. There are, however, species that exist with as many as twenty-five arms.

They all prey upon shellfish, which they straddle and gradually pull open. The bottom surface of the starfish is equipped with five double rows of minute suction cups, called tube feet, with which it moves about and opens oysters, mussels and other shellfish. Anyone who has tried to open an oyster may wonder how a small, apparently weak starfish can accomplish this. The secret lies in the fact that the starfish exerts a steady pull until the shellfish is exhausted. This may continue for as long as forty-eight hours. The starfish can do this because it does not pull with all its tube feet at one time; perhaps one-third of the feet

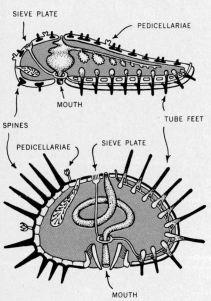

Sea urchins and starfish are closely related and have many structural similarities. These cross-section views of a **starfish arm** (top) and of a **sea urchin** (bottom) provide a good comparison of the two animals. Note that they each have spines, tube feet with a hydraulic-control system, pedicellariae, a mouth in the middle of the bottom surface, and a sieve-plate intake for the hydraulic system.

will exert pressure on the shellfish while the other two-thirds rest. When the working feet grow tired some of the rested feet take over the job, and the result is a relentless attack which the starfish can keep up indefinitely.

When a shellfish is located there can be no escape for it. Once the shell is open, the starfish turns its stomach inside out and inserts it into the shell. Digestion takes place completely outside the body of the starfish and, when the meal is over, the starfish moves off, leaving an empty shell.

The skin of the starfish is covered with delicate skin gills through which it absorbs oxygen from the water. To protect them, short heavy spines project from the upper surface, as well as tiny claws or pincers called pedicellariae. The latter serve to keep small animals from settling on the starfish and sometimes to capture small prey. If a starfish is placed upside down on a person's arm the pedicellariae will grasp the hairs and may be readily felt. Starfish are removed from oyster beds by dragging mops over the bottom. The pedicellariae grasp the mop and the starfish are pulled to the surface.

Starfish, like anemones, have regenerative powers, and if cut in five pieces can grow to be five new starfish under good conditions. For many years this fact was not known, and shellfishermen, believing starfish a threat to their crop, tore them to pieces and threw them back into the ocean. Thus their efforts served only to increase the numbers of starfish. In many regions there are laws that prohibit returning starfish to the water when they have been brought up in shellfish dredges. Instead, they are brought ashore and cast up on the beach to die.

Try Not to Step on This One!

T HE SPINY SEA URCHIN, sometimes called sea egg or vana-vana, is related to the starfish and has the same fundamental structure, although the two do not appear to be at all alike. If we bend the arms of the starfish upward and inward until they meet, it begins to resemble the body of an urchin. The tube feet are present in five double rows and the spines have become very long to protect the urchin from its ever-present enemies.

The common species is very plentiful on sandy bottoms and in coral rocks. Many bathers have received painful wounds when they stepped on or brushed against an urchin. The spines are literally as sharp as needles, and are extremely brittle. It is almost impossible to pull one of these glass-like spines out of flesh. When a spine breaks off under the skin, a purple stain appears. After a few days the spine apparently dissolves and the stain disappears. While quite painful, the wounds are not considered dangerous.

When an urchin is touched on one side, the spines turn in that direction to increase the protection on that side. The spines also collect

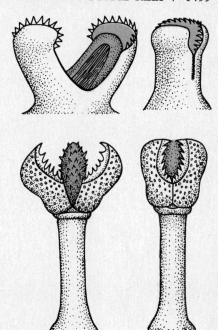

(above)
The **pedicellariae** of both starfish and sea urchins are used mainly for grasping and holding on. These tiny pincers may have either two or three jaws, and some two-jawed types operate like a pair of scissors. Those of the sea urchin are on long stalks.

(below)
Like the anemone, the **starfish** can reproduce a part of itself that has been eaten or torn off by another animal. Under exceptionally good conditions, pieces of starfish can each grow into a whole new starfish.

small bits of seaweed and pass them to the mouth, which is located on the underside of the body.

The tiny claw-like pedicellariae we found on the starfish are present and well-developed in the urchins. They are usually on long stalks and some are equipped with poison glands to aid in capturing prey. The tube feet are longer than the spines and are used with them for locomotion. The mouth of a sea urchin is a marvelously complex structure, called "Aristotle's Lantern". It is formed of five teeth that work together efficiently to scrape vegetation from rocks.

Sea urchins are not completely vegetarian. Occasionally they feed on dead animals found on the ocean floor; less frequently they catch small animals in their pedicellariae. Urchins can bore cavities in coral rocks, but it is a very slow process, sometimes taking years. Apparently the spines are not employed in this boring. The tube feet are used to keep the rock surface clean and remove any loose particles of the rock itself, while the dissolving action of the sea water probably does the actual work of making the cavity.

Spines Instead of Claws

THE SPINY LOBSTER is basically a cave dweller. The south Atlantic species is called a langousta; similar species are found throughout the warmer regions of the world. The rock lobster of Africa is valuable commercially and is shipped all over the world.

The langousta rarely ventures very far from his hole in the coral or the crevice under a coral head. Like the north Atlantic lobster, the langousta is a scavenger; but unlike his northern relatives, he does not have two large claws that make up one-third to one-half of his weight. His antennae, however, have become extended until they are longer than the body and are covered with very sharp spines. Hence the name, "spiny lobster". The spines serve him well for self-protection.

The bulk of the lobsters' diet consists of dead fish and other refuse, snails and small marine animals. They are normally not quick enough to catch live prey but will feed on it when they can. Their diet also includes some algae and eelgrass. Dead fish are commonly used as bait in lobster traps.

Lobsters shed their shells when they have outgrown them, and normally increase in size about fifteen per cent with each shell shedding. A five-year-old lobster will be about ten inches long and has shed perhaps twenty-five times. The lobster goes through a soft-shell stage as crabs do, with the new shell becoming fairly hard in twenty-four hours and fully hardened in six to eight weeks. New shells are considerably brighter in hue than the old ones.

Lobsters normally crawl forward over the bottom, but are able to travel backward very rapidly by snapping their tails. They frequently elude a diver unless they are cornered. Langousta are capable of making

Although the **spiny lobster** lacks the huge protective claws of its North Atlantic relative, its long antennae, covered with prickly spines, are very effective weapons for self-defense.

a hungry predator would expect the butterfly fish to be headed toward the left. Any effort to head him off would cause the predator to turn still farther to the left, while all the time the butterfly fish is headed to the right and should have ample time to escape.

Butterfly fish are seldom seen alone. They travel in pairs or in small schools of several pairs. In moving through the corals they may turn sideways or upside down, and one may occasionally fall behind his companions when distracted by some new or interesting thing. Some butterfly fish are found as far north as the forty-fifth parallel. Some have been seen nibbling parasites from larger fish, as do the cleaning wrasses and some gobies and shrimps. How these "cleaners" determine which fish are safe to approach is a mystery. When a small wrasse picks particles from the teeth of larger fish, it's a little like the lion tamer who sticks his head into the lion's mouth—except that this "lion" may weigh a hundred or a thousand times as much as the "trainer".

Every Sponge Has to Eat

SPONGES ARE familiar to all of us, but many people do not realize that the sponge they buy is actually the skeleton of a group of sponge animals fused into a single large colony. There is no dividing line between its members and no way of telling where one stops and the next begins.

Living sponges grow in a variety of sizes and shapes; most often they appear as irregular lumps of leathery material full of holes. The openings we can see are only a fraction of the total number; the entire surface of a sponge is covered with microscopic openings or pores, much like the pores in our own skin. It is this fact that gives the sponges their name, Porifera, which means "pore bearers".

A sponge may be accurately described as a living filter. Its food consists entirely of microscopic organisms which it removes from the sea water. The visible holes in a sponge are the excurrent openings, through which the water flows after the food materials have been strained out of it. Each excurrent opening and the nearby incurrent openings might be thought of as an individual, but there are no "boundary lines" between one individual and another; they simply merge together.

Sponges assume many shapes, one of the most common being a round, basket-shaped colony. Others may take the form of upright vases or cups, or may simply grow on the ocean floor in an irregular lump.

The current that supplies the sponge with food is produced by "collar cells" within the colony. Each of these cells is equipped with a single long hair, or flagellum, which it waves through the water to create this current. Water is expelled through the excurrent openings and the sea water is sucked in through the incurrent openings.

Living sponge tissue is very soft and almost jelly-like. Without some sort of support a sponge could never grow very large or hold a definite shape. However it has a skeleton composed of many millions of tiny

(below)
Living sponges are found in many shades, and divers may come across sponges of different colors growing together. Unfortunately, the sponges lose their bright tints when dried out for home use.

(bottom)
Iridescent blue stripes identify the the graceful **queen triggerfish.** Its special weapon, consisting of a trigger and spines, is a sufficient deterrent to many attackers.

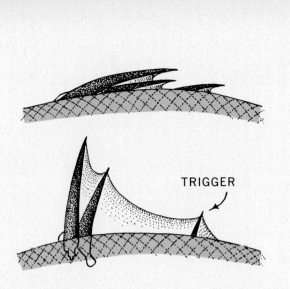

TRIGGER

TRIGGER

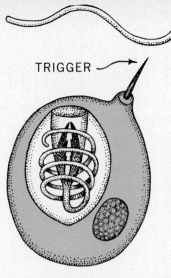

TRIGGER

TRIGGER CELL
BEFORE DISCHARGE

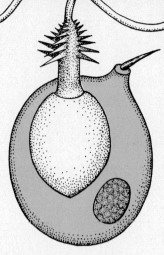

SAME CELL
AFTER DISCHARGE

needle-like structures called spicules. These are produced by special cells and may be made of calcium carbonate, silica or a horny material called spongin. The spicules are one of the main ways of identifying sponges.

Because of variations within a single species, we cannot accurately identify sponges by size, shape, hue or appearance alone. Sponges with calcium carbonate spicules form the chalky or calcareous group; the silica spicules define the glass sponges; and horny sponges, which have spicules of spongin, are the familiar commercial sponges. Spongin is related chemically to silk and animal horn. Natural sponges are tougher and stand wear better than rubber, cellulose or other synthetic sponges. They are widely used for cleaning and polishing. In the past they have served as padding, paintbrushes, mops, and even as substitutes for drinking cups.

Sponges range in size from a fraction of an inch in length to as much as four or five feet. Living colonies may be yellow, red, blue, purple, white, grey or black. Sometimes two sponges of different hues will be found growing together.

Many small animals live within the sponge for protection, and it may become a veritable zoo. As many as 13,500 animals have been found in a single sponge. These included nineteen species of worms, crustaceans, shrimp, copepods and fish.

A Triggerfish Is Full of Surprises

THE TRIGGERFISH have a distinctive method of swimming. The top and bottom fins are swept to one side and then the other, both moving simultaneously. Even when a triggerfish is a long way off and can hardly be seen, this motion identifies it.

Triggerfish also have a very unusual protective device. When an enemy appears the fish raises a spike on its back to a vertical position,

(top, far left)
A unique defense, the **three-spined dorsal fin** on the back of the triggerfish locks rigidly into place when danger threatens. At other times, this fin lies folded down and almost unseen.

(above)
When stimulated, the **nematocysts,** or stinging cells, of fire-corals, anemones and jellyfish discharge a hollow, needlelike "thread" with great force. This thread will penetrate whatever has brushed against the cell and inject a poison that can immobilize fish and cause painful irritations to unwary humans.

where it locks rigidly in place. This spike cannot be folded down and breaks off if enough force is applied. When the second, smaller spike behind it is depressed, they both fold down easily. This smaller spike is called the trigger and gives the triggerfish its name. The spike is similar to the barb on the fishhook. When a predator is unwise enough to attempt to swallow a triggerfish, it will catch in his throat and the two will die together.

The queen triggerfish is the most beautiful of the family and is highlighted with iridescent blue markings. This species is able to change its hue quite rapidly. The fins and tail are long and graceful.

Crabs are a preferred food of the triggerfish but are selected with great care. The eye of the triggerfish is located quite a distance from the mouth. Small crabs present no hazard, but larger ones held in the fish's mouth would reach the eye and blind him. The triggerfish seems to sense this fact and will not attack any crab big enough to endanger its eyes.

All slow-moving fish must have some means of protection. This may be a device to prevent its being swallowed, like that of the triggerfish, or it may simply be good camouflage. Among the best-protected fish in the sea are the porcupine puffer and its relatives. They can inflate themselves with water or air until they are two to three times their normal size, and hopefully too big to be swallowed. As an added precaution, some species have sharp spikes all over their skin which stand out straight when the fish is inflated; a predator would have to be hungry indeed to tackle such a pincushion! Puffers are caught for two reasons. One reason is that they are used in the manufacture of lamps and ornaments. They are simply inflated and allowed to dry thoroughly, then set on a base or fitted with an electric-light bulb. Their other use, perhaps more dignified, is for food, but here is an interesting fact. The liver, skin and gills are highly poisonous. Yet the strip of meat along the spine is edible, delicious and commands a high price when sold as "sea squab". Clearly this is an unusual fish in every way.

The Misunderstood Barracuda

ONE OF THE MOST misunderstood fish is the great barracuda. He has gained a very bad reputation through the years and is feared by seafarers the world over. On the south coast of Cuba, he is respectfully called "the señor". There are few cases where a barracuda has deliberately attacked a bather in the water. Many millions of swimmers are in the water every year with barracuda, although they seldom know of the fish's presence. In cloudy water, or at night, any predatory fish may sense an object moving through the water and attack it without recognizing what it is. It is very foolish and dangerous to swim in tropical waters at twilight or after dark.

Spiky points covering the skin of the **burrfish** warn would-be attackers to keep their distance. When threatened, this versatile fish, also known as the **puffer,** can puff itself up to over twice its normal size. Then its spikes stick out menacingly in all directions.

A coastal species of fairly shallow waters, this broadly striped member of the family of sea basses, *Serranus scriba,* is a bold and aggressive carnivore. It will attack fish larger than itself if they are wounded or mutilated. Its usual abode is in spaces between or under rocks, where it can blend well with the shadows and vegetation.

Although larger and much heavier specimens were once known, most
loggerhead turtles seen today are generally about three feet long and
weigh 300 pounds or less. These marine turtles still breed on some parts
of the coast of the United States, notably around Florida, Georgia and
California. They feed mainly on fish, mollusks and crustaceans.

Barracudas will snap at anything small that suddenly dips into the water. They have been known to bite at oar blades, and it is unwise to rinse one's hands in the water if there are barracudas nearby. If confined in any way they become quite dangerous. One biologist was bitten on the heel when he descended a ladder into a large pen that held a barracuda. This same specimen, in the open ocean, might well have left him alone.

Part of his reputation no doubt comes from the barracuda's appearance. He always seems to be frowning or scowling, and his large undershot jaw is well equipped with very sharp teeth, sometimes over an inch long. As if this were not enough, he has the habit of stretching his jaws open and snapping them shut. This performance never fails to impress divers.

Barracuda will investigate anything new that comes into their section of the ocean and often greet a diver or underwater photographer as soon as he enters the water. This may be largely curiosity. Their silvery tone makes them very hard to see as they merge with the blue of ocean water. They can change their hue to match their surroundings, becoming lightest over sand and darkest among rocks. A barracuda can hang forty or fifty feet behind a diver and watch the proceedings for a long time without being discovered. It is easy to understand the barracuda's interest, since a man-sized fish with all sorts of peculiar equipment is something new. The barracuda never saw a fish that blew so many bubbles!

Barracuda are extremely fast, possibly the fastest fish in the sea, and there are stories of their taking speared fish off the diver's spear before he can retrieve it. Most predators, barracuda included, will attack a disabled fish much more readily than a healthy one. An injured fish swimming among hundreds of others will be pursued even though the predator has shown no previous inclination to feed. Some other fish destroy crippled members of their own species.

After a time, most divers become accustomed to one or two barracuda hanging around and wait until they leave before spearing any fish. Photographers and divers should not wear anything small and shiny that might attract them. Surprisingly, other fish do not run from a barracuda, although he may at any time make a dash into a school of them for a meal. Barracuda have been observed herding fish into a compact school before attacking them. They almost always will come up behind a diver and can sense when he turns toward them and sees them. The fish will then change direction or move off. Until the diver turns toward them, they generally stay and watch. They are quite easy to catch with a shiny metal spoon, and, although generally good to eat, they may be poisonous in a few localities. This may account for some superstitions prevalent in the West Indies.

To make its home, the **yellow-headed jawfish** burrows deep into the sand, having to clear away much debris and often moving many sizable stones. It is one of the few fish that live in holes among the reefs.

The Rough, Tough and Hungry Sharks

SHARKS, WHICH ARE also very curious, are much less common in shallow waters. They are the vultures of the sea and live almost entirely on dead fish and whatever else they find floating on the surface. The list of things which have been found in sharks' stomachs includes tin cans, rocks, shoes, clothing and even a sack of coal. A thirteen-foot tiger shark was found with a fifty-pound turtle in its stomach. Most of their food is obtained on the surface and they show much less interest in things below the surface or on the bottom. They will, however, investigate any strange object they find, including divers.

Vision probably plays a minor part in a shark's life. Its sense of smell is extremely well developed and the olfactory or "smelling" lobes of the brain are much larger than the other lobes. The shark's indifference to pain is astounding. When severely mutilated or even disemboweled, a shark will continue to feed or return to take a baited hook a second time.

Practically every tale of "man-eating sharks" may prove to be false. On the whole, shallow-water sharks are too small, too sluggish or have teeth too small to harm a person. In northern waters, danger from sharks is so slight it can be disregarded. Over two hundred species of sharks are known; only five are considered dangerous and most of those are found offshore. The white shark (Carcharodon) is definitely the most vicious. It is fairly rare in deep waters and practically unknown close to shore. The two largest fish in the ocean are the whale shark and the basking shark. They feed on near-microscopic material and are absolutely harmless to man. In fact, the basking shark has no teeth.

In the final analysis, however, sharks are unpredictable and should not be underestimated. No one really knows what makes a shark vicious at one time or in one area and docile at another time or in another place. Naturally, near slaughterhouse dumps and sewer outlets sharks may become accustomed to feeding, and will think any object in the water is likely to be a food object; but no one yet has determined why the eastern coast of Australia, for instance, is the most dangerous place in the world for shark attacks, and other regions, with as many sharks of the same genus, are considered safe. Normally porpoises will drive sharks away, and one may assume there are no sharks in the water when porpoises are present.

While other creatures of the land and air have changed through the centuries, sharks are practically the same fish they were two hundred million years ago. When seen underwater a shark is a magnificent creature. His swimming is rhythmically graceful. Most species are gunmetal grey, and may have yellow, cat-like eyes.

Remoras, or pilot fish, often attach themselves to sharks. This curious fish has a modified fin on top of its head, which has evolved into an efficient suction cup; it hooks onto sharks for a "free ride". People once

Human swimmers have long feared the sight of the erect fin of a **shark** gliding above the water's surface. In fact, however, of the two hundred known species of sharks, only five are considered dangerous, and these usually inhabit offshore waters, far from oceanside parks and beaches.

A shy creature, the lovely purple-and-gold **fairy bass** is seldom seen, retreating to a crevice on the ocean floor when it senses someone approaching. It lives in holes and dark nooks on the sea bottom.

believed that remoras could guide sharks to a kill and they are still called pilot fish although scientists no longer believe this theory. The remoras probably go along to pick up the crumbs when a shark is feeding.

It is true that sharks are excited by the presence of blood in the water. At such times, they will rush around madly and may bite anything that moves, although they never attack each other. The sharks' well-developed sense of smell is necessary for finding food. Sharks may be attracted by detonating a stick of dynamite underwater, but it is doubtful if the noise alone attracts them. Rather, the fluttering of small fish injured by the blast is transmitted through the water and the sharks come to prey upon them.

Fishes are divided into two groups. The common fishes—salmon, bass, mackerel, cod, tarpon, herring, flatfish, tuna, etc.—have true bones and compose one group. The sharks, skates and rays have skeletons of cartilage and form the other group. The latter group is peculiar in that some species lay eggs the way most fish do, while others bear their young alive. Sharks swim about and are shaped like other fishes, while the skates and rays are flattened, with both eyes on top of their heads, and live on the ocean floor.

Skin Diving for Fun and Study

THE INVENTION of the self-contained underwater breathing devices has aided biologists greatly in their studies of marine life. These devices have also been responsible for a notable increase in the number of sportsmen engaged in underwater spearfishing and skin diving.

The term skin diving refers to the fact that a conventional pressurized diving suit is not used. It is now possible to strap on a compressed air tank and stay under water for an hour or more, without a cumbersome suit and lead-weighted shoes which stir up the bottom and make the study of small, delicate creatures difficult if not impossible. It is also possible to enter coral caves and crevices that would be extremely dangerous if attempted in a typical diving suit. The biologist can explore caves which could not be entered by a suit diver, who must remain upright and is equipped with a vital air hose to the surface that must not be fouled or allowed to chafe on the rocks. The skin diver is also free to swim completely through arches and other formations without backtracking to keep hoses clear, and he can make much better time moving over the bottom than a suit diver.

Compressed-air units can be used by professional or very experienced divers down to three hundred feet or more, but most of the marine student's work will be in much shallower water. Corals and their hordes of inhabitants are found at one hundred and fifty feet or less. Photography without artificial light sources is practical only to a depth of twenty-five or thirty feet. Re-breather-type oxygen units are useful be-

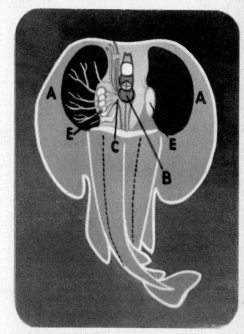

A relative of the shark, the **electric ray** has the ability to store and discharge electricity. Its internal electrical system includes the large electric organs (A), a central electric lobe (B), nerve connections (C), branch sacs (E, left) and eyes (E, right).

(right)
Although this colorful fish may seem to be dressed for a costume party, an encounter with it is liable to be anything but pleasant. Its gaily tinted spines will inject poison into any creature that brushes against them, and for this reason it is commonly known as the **scorpionfish.** Also called lionfish or turkeyfish, it will attack and jab an approaching object with its spines.

(below)
The fierce appearance of a **moray eel** is due to its habit of opening and closing its mouth while breathing. If left alone, it will not attack, but divers who try to hook or spear it will have a battle on their hands.

cause a cloud of bubbles is not released with every breath and the fish do not become so easily alarmed. Changing depth cannot be accomplished quickly with re-breathing outfits, however, and they are much more complicated to use and not as safe as the compressed-air types.

The Fantastic Groupers and Giants

MEMBERS OF the grouper family are common bottom dwellers. They range from one- and two-pounders to huge jewfish weighing from six to eight hundred pounds. These leviathans can be discovered in coral caves, under rocks, or majestically swimming along the bottom. They are generally found living alone. Groupers are carnivorous gluttons and often lie in wait for small fish to swim by. Their speed when they dash out of their hiding places is surprising. Groupers are very well adapted to the life they lead. They are able to change their hue to quite a marked extent and can effect an efficient camouflage. The Nassau grouper is covered with an irregular series of stripes and bars which resembles designs used to disguise ships in World War I.

The mouth and throat of a grouper are truly extraordinary. The open mouth is nearly as wide as the body and the throat is lined with backward-pointing projections which render escape impossible, once a fish is drawn into that cavernous mouth. It is claimed by some that groupers create a current flowing into their mouths which helps to suck in food.

Some of the larger species could conceivably swallow a small boy, but there are no records to indicate that this has ever happened. Groupers live on or near the bottom, feeding on any squid, octopi, crabs or small fish that may come along. They never seem to satisfy their appetites. They are not hard to hook with fishing tackle, but landing them is quite another matter. Groupers and their larger relatives are probably responsible for more "big one that got away" stories than any other fish. They have been known to break or cut through double strands of seventy-five-pound-test wire leaders.

A grouper really comes into its own when it appears on the dinner table. The succulent steaks and fillets of a grouper have no match among northern species and the flaky white meat is unsurpassed anywhere. Grouper frequently finds its way into the stew pot to make fish chowder or bouillabaisse and is enjoyed equally in fine hotels and humble homes.

Groupers and their oversized cousins, the giant jewfish, are sought by spearfishermen for many reasons. They are fairly plentiful, good sport when speared, and look equally good in front of a camera or on the table.

Strange Names That Are Well Deserved

MANY FISH NAMES may at first glance seem rather peculiar, but behind most of them there is a logical explanation. The doctorfish is one of the species found browsing along the coral reefs in schools, stopping now and again to feed on small plants and animal life. This brownish-grey fish bears no resemblance to anything in the medical world, until we take a close look at the base of its tail. On either side is a small projection like a scalpel that is extremely sharp. This fact may be discovered quite by accident if a doctorfish is caught and carelessly handled. Since he always carries this scalpel, the name is appropriate.

The doctorfish is related to the tangs, and some similar form is found in nearly all tropical seas. Sometimes called lancetfish or surgeonfish, it reaches a length of about a foot and is valued as food in some localities. The blue tang of the Caribbean is closely related to the doctorfish and is similar in shape and size. This species is a deep blue and the yellow-orange scalpel is very noticeable. These spines may be extended by the fish and may be employed in defending itself. The doctorfish slashes sideways with its tail when it is caught or speared. Large mixed schools of doctorfish and blue tang are rarities, but in small groups they seem to get along well with each other. Often several species—doctorfish, blue tang and rock beauty—will be seen together.

Beautiful, but a Terrible Nuisance!

HORDES OF SMALL FISH, completely yellow or yellow with a brown stripe down each side, are numerous on the reefs. These fish are so curious that they often become a nuisance to the photographer by swimming up within a few inches of the lens when he is trying to take a picture. The result is much the same as if a finger were accidentally held in front of the lens. A huge out-of-focus blob oc-

(below)
Slow-moving and inoffensive, the **filefish** is protected by its very tough skin, which is used for sandpaper when the fish is caught. Most species inhabit tropical coastal waters. This fantail filefish comes from Hawaii.

(bottom)
A highly valued food fish, the unevenly striped **Nassau grouper** may have inspired the painted camouflage for battleships in World War I. When hooked, groupers fight fiercely and with unbelievable strength.

(top)
These small yellow fish feeding in a school among the corals are, surprisingly, **blue-heads.** When closely inspected, however, the adult males do have a bright blue head, set off by a neat white collar. The females, however, are drabber, having skins of dull yellow-green.

(above)
Almost hidden, scalpel-like projections on each side near the base of the tail give the brownish-grey **doctorfish** its unusual name. It often travels with its relative, the **blue tang,** whose bright orange "scalpel" is easy to spot.

cupies most of the photograph. Occasionally they will swim up to one's face mask. These habits, if nothing else, cause enough interest to make the diver look them up in a fish guide. Imagine his amazement when he learns that these little yellow fish are called blue-heads! The adult male does indeed have a very blue head, nicely separated from the rest of his body by a white collar. Blue-heads seek each other's company and are seen in schools, cruising among the corals or moving slowly across the reef, feeding as they go.

The extreme variations in hue between young and adult blue-heads has caused a great deal of confusion in the past. Bermudians once classed the blue-heads as several separate species, not realizing they were observing the different phases of a single species. To further complicate things, young blue-heads of the same age may be quite dissimilar in appearance. The dark band down each side breaks up at one stage and the fish may go into either a light or a dark phase. Adult female blue-heads are the same size as the males but are a drab greenish-yellow.

Bermuda Chub Like Company

ANOTHER FISH found in schools is the Bermuda chub. Despite its name it is a common visitor to Bahamian waters and the southern coasts of North America. Its curiosity does not match that of the blue-heads, or at least it investigates from a greater distance. Schools of fifty or more fish sometimes split and pass a diver on both sides. It is sometimes called a rudderfish from the habit of following closely under the stern of a boat. Bermuda chub reach a weight of ten pounds or more and are fine sport on a rod and reel. They are scrappy fighters for their size and are a good food fish. They are not speared as often as some other species because of their timid nature. Bermuda chub are a neutral silver-grey and can vary their hue to some extent.

Is It a Plant or an Animal?

MANY MARINE ANIMALS resemble flowers and plants so closely it takes a biologist or trained observer to tell which is which. A group of sessile fan-worms growing in a head of brain coral certainly does not resemble any familiar animal, let alone a group of worms.

The flower-like parts we can see are the gills, which are extended into the water to catch small bits of food and to absorb oxygen from the water. All the important organs of these worms are concentrated at the upper end, and the eyes are located on these gills. Some species are called "feather-duster worms" because of the appearance of the finely-branched feathery gills, and some are called "peacock worms" for their flamboyant appearance. They may only become fully extended at night, when unfortunately no one can see their full finery.

It is doubtful if these worms can see more than simple light and dark areas, but they can detect motion. A diver's shadow will cause them to snap back into their tubes so quickly there can be no doubt as to their identity as animals. Fan-worms build lime tubes in coral heads or among rock formations, and extend only their gills outside these tubes. Tiny hairs, or cilia, line these gills and create a current that brings a supply of diatoms and other food particles to the worms.

Some tube-dwelling worms have developed a growth which effectively closes the opening of their tubes after they have retreated to them. In certain species, this door holds the eggs until they hatch. The plug has a sticky surface to which small bits of sand, shell and debris adhere. When it is in place, it is almost impossible to distinguish the worms from their surroundings.

Some marine worms build their tube burrows in the sand alongside the reef itself. These burrows end in miniature volcano cones, looking a little like Egyptian pyramids. Some of these burrows have a mound at each end, and the worms create a constant current of water through the burrow by moving their cilia and flipper-like appendages. From the water they strain the small organisms on which they live.

Because of the protection afforded and the constant current of sea water, these burrows are preferred dwelling places for smaller creatures. Other species of worms, several kinds of small crabs, clams and even a tiny fish, the goby, are frequent residents of worms' burrows. An added advantage to these tenants is the fact that some worms will refuse to eat larger pieces of food materials and drop them into the bottom of the burrow.

By now we should have become used to meeting strange and peculiar inhabitants of the coral reefs. Is it any wonder to find a fish that "sits" on the bottom and looks more like a snake than a fish? The snakefish is unique. Its body is nearly round and it props itself up on its pectoral fins, as a person leans on his elbows. Its markings blend well with the white sand and coral rocks on which it is found. Black bands break up its outline and only the gaping mouth and bright green eyes stand out.

Another unusual thing about the snakefish is that it cannot float or remain suspended in the water as most fish can. It sinks to the bottom when it stops swimming. Consequently, its progress is erratic. A spurt of energetic swimming will end in a period of inactivity on the ocean floor or convenient rock; then it is off again, darting to the next resting spot.

Snakefish lack air bladders. In most fish this organ is involved in balance and hearing, in making noises and adjusting to changes in the saltiness of the water, and as an oxygen reservoir. But not all of the functions of the air bladder are fully understood. Fish without air bladders, or with damaged ones, lack the buoyancy necessary for normal swimming or suspension in the water. The one exception is the shark, which, lacking this bladder, has a huge oil-filled liver which helps maintain its balance.

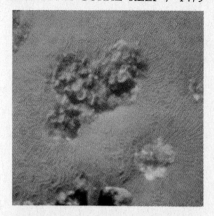

(top)
A casual observer would be puzzled if he tried to identify these marine animals. Resembling clusters of undersea flowers, these sessile **fan-worms** thrive in coral heads. The visible, flowerlike parts are the gills.

(above)
Despite its bottom-dwelling habits and its shape and markings, which look startlingly like those of a real snake, the **snakefish** could not exist outside its watery home. Unable to float like most fish, it swims erratically, sinking to the ocean floor and spending much time resting among coral beds or rocks.

Angelfish Make Perfect Models

ANGELFISH ARE constant companions to the diver working on the reefs. More often than not several will appear soon after the diver arrives and stay nearby as long as he is in the water. They are a bright part of the beauty of the coral reef and are among the prettiest fish in the sea.

Photographers are particularly pleased with angelfish, as their actions seem made to order for photographic purposes. They will swim toward a diver, turn sideways, and stay motionless for a few seconds. Professional models could hardly do any better. There is ample time to focus and shoot, and the angelfish are in a position to show their vivid hues to best advantage. Seen head-on, their extreme thinness is evident. When caught on a fishing line the breadth of their bodies offers so much resistance to the water that the fisherman expects a bigger fish. Angelfish are seldom speared since they offer no challenge even to the most inexperienced skin diver and are not particularly tasty as food.

The French angelfish is a showy member of the family. When young he has vertical yellow stripes. The adult is velvety black with the edge of each scale showing a thin line of bright yellow. The small mouth is bordered by white and light blue areas. Queen angelfish are even more strikingly tinted with golden and bright blue markings. These are popular with tropical-fish hobbyists.

Sea Turtle Ways and Uses

ONE LITTLE SEA TURTLE is more familiar to many people than they realize. From his shell are made many articles in everyday use. Frames for eyeglasses, handles of various instruments, combs and toilet articles are a few of the "tortoise shell" items made of the shells of hawksbill turtles. The thirteen plates of the shell are similar to animal horn and may be softened by applying heat. They may be welded together if care is taken to avoid overheating, which darkens the shell.

The best tortoise shell comes from the Pacific, but turtles are found in all tropical seas and have been used by man for hundreds of years. Some of the treasures brought from the Far East to Rome in Marco Polo's time were made of tortoise shell, and modern treasures of exquisite inlaid work are still being made. In American Colonial days, Captain John Smith reported that a single turtle fed forty men at a sitting. This was probably a green sea turtle, the only type commonly eaten today. Green turtles reach four feet in length and weigh five hundred pounds. In spite of this bulk, they are exceedingly fast in the water and can easily escape a swimmer. Sea turtles are frequently seen sleeping on the surface. When an approaching boat wakes them up, they "crash-dive" almost vertically. The hawksbill is the smallest of the

Smallest of the sea turtles, the **hawksbill turtle,** named for its hawklike head, is full grown at two and a half feet. It is hunted for its beautiful multitoned shell, which can be fashioned into many commercial products.

marine turtles and seldom exceeds thirty inches, weighing about thirty-five pounds.

When turtles come ashore to lay their eggs on sandy beaches they are easily captured. The practice of taking them before they lay their eggs has decreased their numbers alarmingly, and as early as 1620 laws were passed in Bermuda to control the slaughter of turtles. Live turtles are stored and transported on their backs. Many people consider this cruel, but it is necessary to keep them from suffocating. Like a stranded whale, they cannot raise their own weight to draw air into their lungs.

Turtles eat sponges, grasses, mollusks, crustacea and even jellyfish. The hawksbill turtle, which often feeds on the Portuguese man-of-war, keeps his eyes closed while feeding on this jellyfish. Fishermen are aware of this fact and can approach the turtles more readily at this time. Since jellyfish are over ninety per cent water, it seems strange that a turtle bothers with them. It must take thousands of jellyfish to make any kind of meal, in spite of the fact that turtles require extremely little food. It has been estimated that a nine-pound turtle can subsist for a month on a six-ounce banana.

Conservationists are rightfully alarmed at the steady decrease of sea turtles, and the steady and continuous practice of taking all the eggs possible for food. The Bahamas Trust and other societies have transported thousands of baby turtles from Central America in recent years, and have released them at certain spots in the Bahamas. Hopefully, these turtles will come back to the beach of their release when old enough to breed, and colonies will be re-established in the Bahamas.

The Astonishing Fire-coral

MILLEPORA ALCICORNIS is the fire-coral of tropical seas. It is not a true coral and lacks visible "cups" on its surface. It is yellowish-brown, usually with white edges. A confusing quality of the fire-coral is that it grows in so many different forms. By itself it forms flat sheets, spikes and branching arms, and is not too difficult to recognize. However, millepora is an encrusting coral and grows over all sorts of objects on the ocean floor. It can completely cover sea fans. A smooth brown rock, a stick of wood, or ship wreckage may be encrusted with fire-coral.

Divers should not be deceived by the fact that these corals may often be handled without any burning sensation. The palms of the hands may be calloused enough to resist the stinging cells. When more sensitive skin contacts it, however, a painful red welt appears which lasts several days. Unpleasant memories always accompany a lack of knowledge about fire-coral. This type of sting is identical to that of an anemone, jellyfish or Portuguese man-of-war. Their stings are all caused by a tiny hypodermic-needle "gun" called a nematocyst.

(top)
With a unique versatility, the **fire-coral** can assume many shapes, making it hard to recognize. It not only grows alone, in sheets or spikes, but may attach itself to other corals—here it has encrusted itself on a **sea fan**.

(above)
The **French angelfish** is a particularly striking member of its family. It shows off vertical yellow stripes when young, but these disappear as it grows older, to be replaced by black scales, each delicately outlined in bright yellow.

The exact method of discharging a nematocyst is not known. It is caused by an increase in water pressure within the stinging cell, probably produced by a rapid intake of water or a contraction of muscle-like strands. The coiled hollow "thread" is turned inside-out, like the finger of a rubber glove when someone blows into the open end. If the thread is long enough to penetrate a person's skin, he gets a "burn" from the poison that is injected. It is sufficient to paralyze small fish.

The study of marine life seldom requires us to handle objects we find on the bottom in order to identify them. The "look, but don't touch" method of observation is especially wise in areas where fire-coral, anemones, urchins and jellyfish abound. Moray eels may be inside any hole in the coral and can inflict a very painful wound. The only safe rule to follow is to leave things alone until they have been definitely identified.

A New Door to Knowledge

SINCE ANCIENT TIMES men have studied the ocean areas of the world to the best of their ability. After all these years, new facts are being discovered and much is still to be learned. With modern diving equipment, underwater exploration is quite safe and extremely interesting. The sea may hold some of the answers to the problems of overpopulation and dwindling food supplies on earth. It is a beautiful classroom in which one may learn many fascinating things about its strange inhabitants and their relationship to their environment. The ecological balance of a coral reef supplies a vivid example to man who has so often destroyed this balance in his own environment.

PETS

$\mathbf{A}$LTHOUGH SOME PEOPLE may consider pet keeping to be a refinement of civilization, nature furnishes many examples of different types of animals living together for their mutual benefit. Moreover, apes and monkeys sometimes seek the companionship of other animals, and an orphaned animal infant may be adopted and "mothered" by the female of a quite different species—just as baby animals are often brought up and domesticated by humans. It may indeed be true that, to some extent, lower forms of life have always been kept by higher forms; in any event, it is certain that sometime in the distant past, before recorded history, man began to tame wild animals and keep them as pets.

Even if pets frequently seem to be extensions of the owners' personalities, it is well to remember that they *are* animals and that they have—at least in a biological sense—lives of their own. Then too, even if removed from their natural habitats, they participate, as do all living things, in the ecological relationships of our planet. If we observe carefully and are as responsive to them as we expect them to be to us, our pets can doubtless teach us more than we can ever expect to teach them. This is justification enough for the two chapters that follow.

Virtually every kind of animal has at one time or another been a pet, and PETS OF THE WORLD considers the unique and unusual as well as the more familiar animals that have been man's companions and helpers. Ranging from crickets to elephants and from timid mice to ferocious lions, man's pets have provided him with limitless opportunities to experience and explore his kinship with the rest of the animal kingdom.

No animal, however, has for so long, or so exclusively, been associated with man and his dwelling places than has the dog. Although the exact ancestry of this animal is not known, there is reason to believe that it was already living around human habitations tens of thousands of years ago. The recognized breeds existing today have been carefully developed by selective breeding for special characteristics favored by people, and while it is not possible to cover every variety, the chapter entitled DOGS manages to include some of the most outstanding ones.

▶ *Strange and familiar animals that are kept as pets in different parts of the world.*

Pets of the World

ALTHOUGH MOST PEOPLE are familiar only with such pets as cats, dogs and parakeets, there are many people who keep more unusual pets: monkeys, various rodents, reptiles and amphibians. The taming of wild creatures has been going on for many thousands of years. We can do little but guess at how long ago man started keeping wild creatures as pets, because even some of his earliest writings mentioned tamed animals; but there can be no doubt that wild animals were domesticated and kept as pets before the beginning of recorded history in 3600 B.C.

There is some evidence that, even before man evolved to the state in which we find him today, lower forms of life may have been kept by higher forms. Evidence supporting such a belief can be found in the fact that apes and monkeys, and even other creatures, occasionally seek the companionship of another species just as a lonely person might feel love and compassion for a dog or cat. This is especially true of those animals that are normally gregarious and which for some reason or another are deprived of the chance to associate with others of their species. Maternal instincts are especially strong in all creatures, and experienced zoo keepers can tell many instances of lactating mammals nursing, caring for and raising, as though they were their own offspring, infants of some quite different species. Extremes of cats raising mice are not even uncommon.

Long before ancient man learned to record history, he tamed animals to protect, feed, serve or amuse him. Most pets are kept chiefly for their companionship: whether it crawls, hops, walks, flies or swims, nearly every kind of animal is valued as a pet. (Top right) **Chipmunks** are some of the semiwild animals that live near, but not with, man. These beautiful rodents will often take food from the hand, but it requires much patience from the human and much trust from the chipmunk.

mel hunter

Sometimes Closeness Benefits Both Parties

Another aspect of animals living with those of a different group is that association known as symbiosis (sym—together: biosis—existence). This is the living together, for mutual benefit, of two different species. There are examples of such relationships being vital to one or even both species involved. For example, almost everyone has heard of the hermit crabs that wiggle their soft bodies into the empty whorls of seashells and then catch and "plant" a living sea anemone on top. The anemone attracts living food while also serving to camouflage the unusual household from the roving eyes of predators. Crab and anemone share the meals, and the crab protects the anemone with its sharp pincers. There are ants that carry about, feed and defend tiny primitive insects known as aphids, because they relish the honey-like substance which is exuded by the aphids. There are numerous examples of animals that thus live together. Egrets and other small birds perch on the backs of mighty elephants and buffaloes picking ticks and other parasites from the animals' hides; other birds pop in and out of the spread jaws of crocodiles and act as "living toothbrushes". The larger animals derive some protection from the birds, which fly up in alarm at the approach of danger, thus warning their hosts.

Generally speaking, the animals which have most successfully adapted to living in conjunction with man are those creatures which normally live in groups. These animals are accustomed to body contact by being rubbed, jostled and sometimes groomed, whereas those animals which customarily live solitary lives have difficulty in overcoming their innate fear of being touched. In fact, some animals not only enjoy companionship, but actually require it, as is sadly proved when certain social animals die of loneliness when kept isolated from their fellows. When left alone, monkeys become attached to wooden dolls which they fondle and love to such a degree that they will fiercely defend them. Another example is the passenger pigeon which once flew over North America in flocks composed of billions of individuals. Man ruthlessly reduced its numbers to such an extent that, even though there

(left)
Caracalla, a Roman Emperor, had a pet **lion** named Scimitar that slept at the foot of his bed and sat next to him at the table. For most people, however, a lion would be an impractical pet; when the cub becomes an adult, the meat bills become huge.

(below)
Although they cannot be held or petted and they neither purr nor chirp, **tropical fish** are increasingly popular pets. There is a vast variety of colors and shapes, and an aquarium teaches some basic principles of ecology.

were a few small groups left when the public finally took notice, the species was doomed to extinction. Without the great flocks the remaining individuals lost the capacity to survive. The last passenger pigeon, named Martha, died in the Cincinnati Zoo on 1 September, 1914.

Man is responsible for a depressingly long list of animals which he has affected by his encroachment upon their native habitats. This has resulted in the disappearance of certain animals from the face of the earth. On the other hand there are some animals which have become so dependent on man for so long that they would perish without his assistance. Some animals, such as the worthy cow and virtually indestructible goat, appear to have been saved from extinction by domestication, for their wild ancestors can no longer be found. We should, therefore, be extremely careful which animals we try to press into our service or advertise as pets; we may destroy their wild kind forever.

Just What Is a Pet?

THERE ARE MANY varied conceptions of just what constitutes a pet. In the strict sense of the word, according to Webster's unabridged dictionary, a pet is a domesticated animal kept to fondle and play with. However, the word holds different meanings to different people. There are many who would argue that their aquarium of tropical fish brings them great pleasure and joy, and others call wild creatures pets when they are able to entice them to come to feeding stations near their windows or to feed directly from their hands. Since the origin of the word in itself is highly uncertain it ought not perhaps to surprise us if it is open to widely differing interpretations.

Although only relatively few of all the known species are regularly kept as pets, it is a fact that comparatively few intelligent creatures are incapable of being tamed and trained if taken when young and placed in the hands of a well-informed and conscientious handler. The ferocious badger and wolf; flesh-eating lions and tigers; large birds of prey; all these have been successfully raised by man to become loving

Raptors, or birds of prey such as **hawks,** can be exciting pets if carefully raised. All raptors, however, can be dangerous and should be trained and handled by adults. Although they eat mainly rodents and snakes, most birds of prey are being poisoned to the edge of extinction in the mistaken belief that they damage poultry and other livestock.

and affectionate—at least to their trainers. In a sense, then, it would be safe to say that almost all animals have at some time, somewhere, been kept as pets.

It is generally agreed, though, that some groups of animals have a greater capacity or ability to adapt and associate with man as pets. But it must be pointed out that animals are individuals, and temperaments vary from one animal to another of the same species or even of the very same litter; and they are subject to moods, just as we are. The observer must therefore be careful not to generalize and jump to conclusions. What may be true for one particular individual cannot be considered characteristic of the entire species.

In my experiences with animals in their natural habitat, under domestication, in zoological parks and as pets, I think that for a wild animal to be classified as a pet, perhaps we should establish certain criteria that, when met, would justify applying the term "pet" to an animal: it should not run away, even when it has the opportunity to do so; it should not harm its keeper; most of all it should show some affectionate response to its human "friends". The mere fact of captivity, if we accept these criteria, does *not* make an animal a pet!

What Makes a Good Pet Owner?

DIFFERENT ANIMALS require varying degrees of human training if they are to be won over to man's way of living. Not all people have the qualifications to be pet owners. A pet owner must be prudent, have sufficient time to care for and play with his pet, have an active enthusiasm and diligence. He must possess a retentive memory to note the animal's reaction to different circumstances; and he must keep his own temper under control at all times.

Unlike a bicycle a pet requires daily attention. If you cannot make the animal at least as happy as it would be in its natural environment, then it would be better if you did not keep a pet. Successful pet owners are those who are dedicated. You will be solely responsible for its welfare, its food, shelter and well-being.

Some Pets Are Helpful in Hunting

LONG BEFORE THE INVENTION of the bow and arrow our early ancestors observed that natural predators were much better equipped than man to capture prey. Falconry, the art of training and using birds of prey for hunting and later for sport, had its origin in China more than 4,000 years ago. Falconry reached its peak during the Middle Ages, during which time an elaborate hierarchy evolved in which different types of birds were allotted to people depending on their rank in society. To kings went the majestic eagles, princes carried gyrfalcons, earls had peregrines; their servants were permitted only kestrels.

Throughout the ages nearly every type of bird of prey has been trained by man for sport. Of all these, the peregrine falcon, characterized by long, narrow, pointed wings and brown eyes, is without doubt the master of the high open sky. Its speed has been recorded with instruments as reaching 180 miles per hour.

Falconry is now a rare sport, despite a small and possibly growing band of enthusiasts in Europe. That it should have declined so greatly is not surprising in view of the vast amount of time and patience necessary for training these birds. Modern society, in general, does not provide the opportunities for it to become a flourishing sport.

Cheetahs, also known as hunting leopards, are related to the cats, but differ in being unable to retract their claws. They are creatures of great beauty and grace, prodigious abilities and a reportedly gentle disposition. Cheetahs, native to open savannahs from India to southern Africa, hold the distinction of being the swiftest of all mammals. Their gentleness, coupled with agility and a speed of sixty miles per hour over very short distances, are reasons why this animal has, for ages, been trained for antelope hunting. Unfortunately, cheetahs are becoming increasingly rare because of their continuing desirability and their failure to breed in captivity.

Some Are Better Fishermen than Humans

CORMORANTS ARE LONG-BODIED, long-necked birds with well-developed throat pouches which have a nearly cosmopolitan distribution. They are found in lakes, marshes and especially along the seacoasts. Long ago it was discovered that hand-raised birds could be taught to pursue, catch and deliver to their masters fish from the open sea. To prevent the birds from swallowing the fish, a metal ring is fixed around their necks. It is small enough to keep from slipping over their heads, but loose enough to permit the birds to breathe and swallow tiny fish. In some cases the rings are affixed only while the birds are fishing and in others they are worn permanently. Cormorants will fish at night under the glare of torches secured in boats. Unlike

(bottom left)
Kestrels are found in every continent except Australia. The American kestrel, also called the sparrow hawk, ranges from the tip of South America to Alaska. The Old World kestrel, shown here, was once used as a hunting bird; because of its small size, it was the only hunting bird allowed to people not of noble blood.

(bottom right)
A **striped hyena** may look like a dog, but it is much too savage to make a good pet. Hyenas prowl in packs by night, eating dead animals, and their weird cry, which sounds like an insane laugh, is usually all the warning other animals need to get safely away. Hyenas have powerful, bone-crushing jaws.

some fishing birds that dive into the water to catch fish, cormorants actually swim after them, using their large, webbed feet. When ashore they like to roost on the gunwales of the master's docked boat. They make highly intelligent pets and follow their owners about.

Hunting with natural enemies, contrary to popular belief, is in no way cruel and unsportsmanlike. In pursuing game with modern firearms, an animal's natural means of self-preservation are of little value. It cannot cope with the situation. In many instances, game escapes wounded and dies a lingering death. Since game animals are not accustomed to the report of firearms, they tend to emigrate from areas frequently hunted. But this is not so when natural enemies are used. With these it is usually a clean kill or a clean miss. Game animals are accustomed to seeing these predators as part of their natural environment, and, as a result, are equipped to compete for survival. Also it is generally the weak individuals that are caught, leaving the stronger ones for the propagation of the species. Egyptians have written accounts describing the training of hyenas as hunting animals, much as dogs are used by hunters today.

Pets May Even Have a Cash Value

THE PERUVIAN CORMORANT, native to the west coast of Central and South America, is one of the chief producers of nitrogen-rich guano, much in demand as a fertilizer all over the world.

Man has realized since earliest times that by domesticating certain species able to provide him with food and raw materials he would need to spend less time in hunting. Most of our present farm livestock and fowl had such origins. Included are beef cattle, dairy cows, hogs, sheep, goats, chickens, guinea fowl, ducks and geese. Other animals, such as sheep, goats, Angora rabbits and more recently the chinchilla and mink, have been kept and bred by man for their fur.

Hamsters, mice and guinea pigs are noted not only for their gentleness, cleanliness and devoted affection to the owners, but also for the part they play in experimental research in medicine.

Millions of Hamsters with a Single Ancestor!

HAMSTERS ARE PARTICULARLY INTERESTING because all the domesticated strains have been developed, during a few decades, from a single litter of twelve individuals. These were discovered in 1930 by a professor at the Hebrew University in Jerusalem who, near the village of Aleppo in Syria, found the mother and her youngsters at the end of an eight-foot burrow. The hamster is able to stuff great quantities of food in special folds of skin called cheek pouches. From this the hamster derived its name, coming from the German word *hamstern* meaning to hoard. They are able to carry *up to one-half their weight*

Gentle and curious, **hamsters** are among the most popular pets. Although one species of these short-tailed rodents burrows all over Europe and Asia, the type of hamsters we have as pets today are all the offspring of a single litter found in 1930.

within these pouches! They are ideal both for pets and laboratory animals in that they are clean, multiply rapidly (sixteen-day gestation period), have a genial disposition and a friendly, inquisitive attitude. It is no wonder, then, that the hamster enjoys great popularity.

The More Pets, the Fewer Pests

IN INDIA a member of the civet tribe was long ago tamed and fully domesticated. This is the mongoose, a nondescript little animal that will kill rats, mice and snakes—even venomous ones. Bright, alert and intelligent, mongooses will breed in captivity and live around the house like farm dogs and cats. They patrol regularly at night, pouncing upon all small intruders. Their importation into North America is absolutely forbidden—no matter for what purpose. Once introduced, mongooses might destroy the entire small natural fauna and become an ineradicable pest to poultry and other bird and mammal breeders. They were taken to the West Indian islands in the last century in an effort to exterminate the rats that swarmed everywhere destroying the crops. Instead they took to the trees and cleaned out the birds and other small natural indigenous ground fauna, then went to work on the chickens and other domestic animals. Mongooses are a terrible menace there but they are a great boon in their own country where they help to control the snakes.

In other countries snakes are kept as pets to keep down rodent populations. Fishes are kept in ornamental pools and other bodies of water to feed on mosquito larvae; in some tropical countries chameleons are kept near open-air meat markets to feed on the flies attracted by the hanging meat.

House geckos, particularly of the genus *Hemidactylus,* are among the few animals that benefit from living with man and which actually seek out his dwellings for permanent residence. The small lizards live behind curtains, in cracks and between reeds in native dwellings; they come out at night, scampering about the walls and ceilings, to snatch up mosquitoes, flies and small moths attracted by the light. They are delightful, entirely harmless animals that can be taught to eat from one's hand. It is easy to understand why their presence is encouraged.

These Burglar Alarms Are Alive

DIVERSE ANIMALS have been taken from the wild, domesticated and trained by man in an effort to utilize their more acute senses to detect the invasion of intruders. Americans and Europeans use only dogs for this purpose as a rule. But elsewhere other animals are given the same task.

Among these are the crickets which the Chinese keep in exquisite cages made from young bamboo twigs. These are either kept on the

Valuable as a rat-catcher in India, the **mongoose** cannot be brought into North America. If it escaped and became wild, this swift hunter, which can kill cobras, would soon destroy our beneficial small animals and birds.

Lizards, silent and not very affectionate, can often be trained, but even those that can't will still make good pets. Horned toads (actuallly lizards) are popular in the southwestern United States, and in some tropical areas geckos are encouraged to live in houses, where they prowl walls and ceilings at night, eating bothersome insects.

floor or hung from the ceiling of the living room, like mobiles. Some cages are constructed like miniature doll houses. The cricket emits a high-pitched trill, made by rubbing the forewings together. When an unfamiliar noise or vibration is present, their singing ceases, thus alerting the household that something may be amiss.

In some areas of the tropics large lizards, namely monitors of the genus *Varanus*, are kept tied to the porches of European dwellings to deter intruders. These large lizards are feared with good reason, for when molested, they use their long, slender, muscular tails as whips which can inflict pain and injury.

Beasts of Burden Can Be Pets Too

NO PERSON CAN SAY when man first began to domesticate wild animals to help him in his daily tasks and in transport; but the list of creatures thus employed is long and varied, ranging from the relatively small husky dog which the Eskimos use to pull their sleds to the gigantic elephant of India and Africa. Animals are thus employed in similar ways by practically every group of people.

Many Pets Are Kept for Their Beauty

IN THIS CATEGORY are those popular cage birds which represent a compromise between the affection and companionship of pets that can be easily touched and fondled and the more easily cared for, yet

(bottom right)
Wingless and only one-tenth of an inch long, **fleas** make amazing leaps of thirteen inches, powered by their exceptionally strong hind legs. This tremendous power enables the insects to pull miniature wagons and carts and also, when trained, to perform jumping tricks similar to those of circus acts. If performers in a **flea circus** could be enlarged to proportional human size, theirs would certainly be the most exciting show on earth, with performers jumping hundreds of yards at each bound.

(above)
Most **monitors** reach a length of three feet, but some types grow twice as long. These tropical meat-eating lizards are often leashed to a porch as "watch dogs." Intruders think twice before risking blows from a monitor's powerful tail.

impersonal, tropical fish. Nevertheless, in some instances cage birds become quite affectionate toward their owners and at times even playful. Above all they are esteemed primarily because of their brilliant plumage, for their singing—or both.

The largest group of cage birds is that of the finches, which include the popular golden canary. Canaries were popular as pets in Spain, Portugal, Italy and other Mediterranean countries as long ago as the fourteenth century. The "normal" yellow hue is caused by an absence of melanin in the plumage. It was soon learned that amazing variations could be produced by selective breeding and specialized diets; grey birds with orange breasts, speckled grey and white and pure white varieties. The most famous breeding grounds of the popular canary is the Harz Mountain region of Germany. Their chief claim to fame is their song; the males, and only the males, are capable of rendering beautiful warbles and trills.

Other finches are attractive cousins of the canary, and their popularity is steadily growing. They are hardy birds and can live as long as twenty years.

At the present time the most popular cage bird in much of the world is the parakeet, also known as the budgerigar or "budgie". The name comes from the Australian native tongue meaning "pretty bird".

Formerly parakeets were known in the United States as exotic curiosities, being imported directly from their native home of Australia. In 1933, the United States Government passed a law (no longer in effect) which forbade the import of all members of the parrot family because they were discovered to be the carriers of *psittacosis*, a disease communicable to man. This ban caused American fanciers to begin breeding experiments that proved very successful. Due to selective breeding we now have the extensive variety of hues common today—all developed from birds that were originally green.

Parakeets make nearly ideal pets. They have an infinite variety of gay hues, make a pleasing chatter and may even sing a few notes. They delight in climbing on their owners when they are released from the cage for exercise.

(top left)
Because of their present variety of color, it is hard to realize that all **parakeets** originally were green. The native home of these small members of the parrot family is Australia.

(top center)
Wild Canaries are singing finches native to the Canary Islands, near the coast of Africa. Selective breeding resulted in the bright yellow cage variety, which were kept as pets as early as the fourteenth century in some Mediterranean countries.

(top right)
This is probably the most gorgeous of all the hundreds of species of **finches**. It comes from Australia, and there are varieties with red, gold, brown and black foreheads. Finches are hardy birds that live up to twenty years.

Flamboyant multi-hued birds such as the males of the pheasant and pea-fowl families have added much beauty to the grounds and gardens of their owners. The original home of these birds is the Orient.

Silent Pets Are Popular Too

WITHIN RECENT YEARS the aquarium has taken a definite place in many homes, and is especially recommended for those who become exasperated by noisy, more demanding pets. Though fish don't return their owners' affection, a beautifully arranged aquarium with some attractive and interesting fishes as inhabitants does much to add life and enjoyment to a home. They are popular because they can be inexpensive to begin and maintain, do not require constant attention, and provide pleasant entertainment. Indeed, even a small aquarium can exert an almost hypnotic effect of calm. Much pleasure can be derived from observing the silent activity of smoothly gliding or darting fishes.

Several species of fish have been fully domesticated by man and there are numerous records of people keeping individual fishes of many kinds in confinement. There is an account of a man from Scotland who kept an eel in a bowl in his home for sixty years! Many fishes have been trained to answer the ringing of a bell or a tapping on the container in which they live. The most remarkable example were probably the royal carp, kept in the garden of the palace of Fontaine-bleau in France. These came to be fed when a bell was rung and even learned to take food from a person's hand. Goldfish are members of the carp family and have been used for centuries as living ornaments in garden pools.

Antics and Companionship Rate High

SEA LIONS, SEALS AND BEARS have become popular "pets" in circuses within the last century. They have an amazing ability to learn and can be trained to perform many tricks. Animal trainers have taught quite a variety of animals to perform circus acts for the enjoyment of the audience.

The Romans taught apes to ride dogs and drive chariots and they were the first Europeans to teach elephants to perform in circuses. Even tiny fleas have been taught tricks similar to those of circus acts and can even be harnessed to pull tiny wagons.

Pets perform a very important role by being companions for lonely persons, and can provide an escape from boredom for the sick or invalids. Children, by learning to care for and love their pets, acquire a relationship which teaches them responsibility and exposes them to the natural functions of living creatures.

Caracalla, a Roman Emperor, was particularly fond of his pet lion, called Scimitar, which sat with him at the table while he dined, and slept nightly at the foot of his bed.

The glorious hues and unusual shapes of the common **goldfish** resulted from careful selective breeding. Goldfish are descended from dull, blue-brown Chinese carp, just as golden canaries are descended from wild Canary Island finches.

Man's Near-universal Companion

Dogs are undoubtedly the commonest of all pets; there is probably no human community in the world that does not have some dogs. There is an incredible variety of shapes, shades and sizes, and from these some three hundred distinct types, that breed true, have been developed throughout the ages. Some of our present breeds can be traced to prehistoric times; spaniel bones have been found in Swiss lake-dwellings of the late Stone Age. Other dogs, such as the greyhound, the Afghan hound and the dachshund, are depicted in ancient Egyptian paintings. Poodles were clipped to resemble lions by the ancient Assyrians.

Dogs perform such helpful activities as hunting, guarding property, herding cattle and sheep, pulling dog sleds and leading the blind, in addition to being devoted and friendly companions.

Monkeys Have Entertained Us for Years

At all periods of history, many types of monkeys and monkey-like creatures have been kept not only as pets, but even as members of man's households. There are, however, some groups that are quite unable to get along outside their own specialized environment. Yet the list of animals customarily kept in human households throughout the world usually comes as a great surprise to us.

Chimpanzees of up to about five years of age, for instance, have been kept as pets in Africa for centuries. There is no evidence, however, that they were exported like the baboon, rhinoceros and other exotic animals from their native equatorial Africa to other countries in early times.

Today chimps have become one of the most outstanding pets of the world, and many books have been written about them. When raised in a human environment, they prove themselves capable of mastering roller-skating, bicycle riding and certain household duties such as sweeping and painting.

The ancient Egyptians apparently managed to train baboons to do

(top left)
Dogs have been man's helpers and pets for over twelve thousand years. The **German shepherd,** pictured here, is among the most intelligent of several hundred distinctly different breeds of dogs.

(top right)
Only two species of **elephants** have survived to modern times: the Asian elephant, the most frequently tamed, and the African elephant, the larger of the two. The biggest, strongest land animal is a strict vegetarian. It has been used in circuses since Roman times.

(below)
Baboons are large, ground-dwelling monkeys that range across most of Africa. At least six, and sometimes as many as a dozen, species are generally recognized. They are dangerous in the wild, but occasionally they can become quite tame in captivity. The ancient Egyptians were able to train some baboons to do household chores.

domestic duties. South America is not unlike the African and Oriental tropics. Its own numerous kinds of monkeys are common in the homes of its indigenous people and those of the Latin-Americans. Among these are some of our most popular pets, notably the woolly monkey, which looks very much like an old man, and the agile squirrel monkeys and spider monkeys. New World monkeys do not, on the whole, have the intelligence of those from the Old World, but some, like the little organ-grinder Capuchin, or ring-tailed monkey, make lively and entertaining pets and have exhibited remarkable mechanical abilities.

In the forests of South America dwell a host of tiny long-tailed creatures, the marmosets, which range in size from that of a squirrel down to that of a large mouse. Some marmosets are very attractive, and the golden lion marmoset is one of the most brightly tinted of all mammals. When the Spanish and Portuguese first reached the shores of the New World, they found these marvelous creatures living as pets in the houses of the Amerindians and sent some to Europe where they were welcomed as pets by the wealthy. Clean, easily tamed and small, marmosets are also intelligent and extremely courageous. They will chatter and scream at any adversary, however big, and will attempt to defend their beloved owners with tiny needle-sharp teeth and scroll-like claws.

Related to the apes and the monkeys are the lemurs of Madagascar. The best-known is the *Mac* or ring-tailed lemur. Since the war, however, they have become rare even in zoos. The Malagasy Republic, in an effort to prevent their lemurs' total extinction, has completely banned both the export and the killing of these animals which form a primate group not to be found elsewhere in the world.

An Old, Old Friend of Man

THE HISTORY OF THE HORSE is a fascinating one indeed. It began in the most ancient times, during the Ice Age. Man was then a hunter and some of the animals available to him were various kinds of horses which roamed the plains and prairies in large herds. It has been shown through archaeological discoveries that sometime between the last retreat of the polar ice and the dawn of primitive civilization, the nomads of the central Asiatic steppes tamed and domesticated the wild horse.

The horse is a unique, highly advanced and specialized animal that has been used by man in almost every imaginable climate—from the hottest deserts to the freezing plateau of the Antarctic continent.

In Java, West Africa and Haiti, and some other places as well, there are ponies that can climb precipitous rocky crags. The only thing that horses really cannot cope with are the wet equatorial forests. That is, their weight causes their relatively small feet to sink in marshy areas.

Horses are of all sizes, and a variety of hues and marking patterns.

Some, such as the Shetland pony, have woolly coats. Miniature horses have recently begun to appear—apparently true mutations. In the days of chivalry, monumental strains of horses, the Shire, the Percheron and the Belgique, were bred as war horses able to carry the great weight of knights encased in their full battle array. Their immense strength has ensured their employment for pulling great loads, even in the present century: the record in size was a Shire that weighed almost two tons.

The somewhat ungainly, often rather tattered-looking reindeer is possibly the most remarkable and useful of all man's domestic animals. A great many serviceable items can be produced from it. Many products are obtained from its horns, skin, fur and hair, hooves, sinews, milk and flesh. A reindeer can carry a man of average weight for several days, and can pull twice its weight on a sled over snow for forty-eight hours. Reindeer could be considered a domesticated strain of the caribou, found around the world in the Arctic regions. In fact, some scientists consider them all to be the same species.

We Find Many Pets Among the Carnivores

SPREAD OVER ALMOST ALL THE WORLD we find an enormous group of mammals known as the carnivores. These are mostly fierce, meat-eating hunters, and their variety is enormous. Many species are easily tamed and playful, and a great number of the smaller ones make fine pets.

All truly domesticated cats seem to have stemmed from one of, at most, three sources: first, the wild cat of the unforested part of North Africa known to science as *Felis lybica,* which is just a wild tabby-cat. Secondly, some blood may have been contributed by this animal's very

(above)
The first "house cat" was apparently a **genet,** not a true cat at all. Nocturnal forest prowlers in Spain, France and parts of Africa, genets are skilled hunters that, if tamed when young, will keep a house free of vermin.

(right)
Reindeer, or domesticated caribou, are unique in that males and females both have antlers. They ranged over Europe during the Ice Age, but they are found today only in arctic regions. As Plains Indians once depended on buffalo, many Eskimos, Siberians and Laplanders depend on reindeer, and use them as thoroughly.

near cousin, *Felis ocreata* of the African forest. Then there are those who contend that the Burmese-Siamese breeds also have a strain of some other wild species from South-east Asia. One eminent expert even suggested that there was once a small blotched cat in Europe that gave us the calico strain that still persists. It is interesting to note that the true wild cat, *Felis sylvestris,* of Europe (which is still found in Scotland), may always have been no more than a distant relative of the domestic cat—never an ancestor.

The first "cat" to be truly domesticated (in ancient Egypt) now appears not to have been a cat at all but a genet, a kind of civet. Furthermore, until Roman times the animals called "cats" in Europe (Spain, Sardinia, Corsica, Provence, Italy and Sicily) were either genets or still another animal, the polecat or ferret, a weasel called *ailuros* in Greek. In country districts throughout northern and central Europe, ferrets are popular pets. The Nubians and Abyssinians seem first to have tamed the cat that we now know. The ancient Egyptians used it to prevent mice and other rodents from making devastating inroads into their well-stocked granaries.

American Settlers Kept Useful Pets

WHEN THE COLONISTS ARRIVED in North America they· found neither polecats nor burrowing rabbits, such as are common in Europe. Soon they began to have as much trouble with rats and other indigenous rodents as their ancestors had had with the rabbits. Since cats were far from numerous, they adopted another animal that seems even more unlikely as a pet around the house than the ferret. This was the mink. Today, of course, the mink is no longer kept as a domestic animal but is bred by the millions, in tones ranging from black to white, blue to cream and orange to rich browns, for use in the fur industry.

(top left)
A domesticated albino polecat, the European **ferret** has long been used to chase rabbits from their burrows **(ferretting).** In many parts of Europe it is also a popular pet, earning its keep by catching rats and other pests.

(top right)
The Nubians and Abyssinians seem to have first domesticated the common cat we know today, although the ancestry of this **Siamese cat** may include a strain of some Southeast Asian species. While there is great variation in coloring among common house cats, the tabby is the most familiar and all other shades and patterns are mutations developed after domestication.

The earliest Europeans in North America found skunks; but instead of retreating in panic as the average modern city dweller would do, they encouraged these little animals to take up residence around their farmsteads where they earned their keep by keeping down pests. Skunks make excellent pets indeed, perhaps one of the best pets of all North American wild animals. Generally it is essential that the scent glands be surgically removed. If this is done the animal must *not* be turned loose in the wild, for without his defensive mechanism he would become easy prey for his enemies. The skunk is the farmer's friend, as it feeds on small rodents and many kinds of injurious insects.

The raccoon and its relatives, the kinkajou and coatimundi, are furry creatures characterized by their curiosity. If caught young, they tame readily and make wonderful pets. The raccoon is so active and inquisitive that it can literally destroy a household if left unattended. Raccoons seem to have the ability to get into everything, spilling, turning over and taking apart whatever they find during the course of their investigations.

Kinkajous are engaging beasts, having some of the qualities of monkeys, raccoons and cats. They are also destructive if left unattended.

Coatimundis resemble raccoons in many ways, but the long upturned nose gives the coatimundi a slightly comical appearance. Like the raccoon and kinkajou, coatis are infinitely inquisitive and manage to get their noses into everything. All of these furry creatures respond well to gentle handling and apparently enjoy their association with their owners.

When the Spanish invaders first reached the Incas in Peru, they found the dark windowless huts of the peasants full of little, squeaking, mumbling, twittering animals that scampered away from their feet when they entered. They were tail-less, had big heads and frightened-looking eyes. Their short limbs had only four toes behind and three in front, and they were black, reddish brown, or *agouti* (an overall brindled effect). The people of the Andes used these animals for food, besides keeping them as pets. They multiplied amazingly fast, were vegetarians and never ran away. They had no offensive scent, never bit, were ap-

(bottom left)
A member of the weasel family, the European **polecat** has a long, slender body and short legs. Like the domesticated ferret, it may sometimes be taught to catch rabbits.

(bottom right)
Mink are very swift, large water-weasels. Although tame mink are now rare, they make good pets. The early American colonists kept these courageous hunters around their homes to catch rats and other rodents.

(below)
Although neither a pig nor from Guinea, the **Peruvian cavy** has come to be called the **guinea pig.** Originally domesticated by the ancient Incas, who ate them, we use these gentle, harmless rodents for medical research or simply as very popular pets.

parently impervious to cold and utterly docile. Someone, said to be a Hollander, acquired some of these worried-looking little creatures in the earliest days of the discovery of the Americas and took them back to Europe, where they were called guinea pigs, just why, nobody knows.

Everyone Knows a Rabbit

TAMED RABBITS AND HARES may be some of our oldest pets and domestic animals. They appear to have been bred in captivity since prehistoric times. They are easy to house and feed, and multiply very rapidly. There are many species scattered throughout Eurasia and North America down to Central America. Rabbits are useful in many ways. They are easy to feed and produce very good meat, but probably their greatest use comes from their fur. The substance we know as felt, used especially for the manufacture of hats, is made from rabbit fur. Rabbits vary greatly in size and hue. The silky-haired Angoras can be plucked regularly, and the fleece spun directly into a beautiful soft yarn; but many other species of rabbits do not do well in captivity. Consequently, we have the saying that domestic rabbits are one of the easiest animals to keep, and wild ones one of the most difficult.

A Pet from Australia

AUSTRALIA IS THE HOME of some special pets that are found living naturally nowhere else in the world. Unfortunately, rabbits, foxes, dogs and cats have been introduced into Australia, and these, along with sheep, cattle, buffalo, barbed-wire fences and modern cities have almost eliminated some of these wonderful creatures. One of these rare animals is the koala.

Shortly after Australia was discovered and began to be settled, some unknown genius made a model of a koala, either by stuffing an actual skin or by constructing one from sheepskin. This model, sent to Europe, proved so enchanting a toy that it immediately came into great demand, and the whole industry of "teddy-bears" began. Today

(top left)
Because it was the model for the teddy bear, many people think the **koala,** a kind of possum, would be a cuddly pet. Actually, this rare marsupial is generally neither friendly nor intelligent. Adults reach two feet in length and carry their young "piggyback" as they browse through eucalyptus trees.

(top right)
A tree-dwelling South and Central American relative of the raccoon, the **kinkajou** makes a delightful pet if tamed when young. It is highly curious, however, and if left alone will take things apart just to explore them.

the teddy-bear is still popular, but the original animal upon which it was patterned has become so scarce as to be in danger of extinction. The koala, actually a kind of possum, is a marsupial, and despite its cute appearance is neither very bright nor particularly friendly. In fact, it can inflict a nasty bite and has very strong sharp claws.

Koalas are now strictly protected, and forests of the eucalyptus trees on which they feed have been set aside for them.

The Biggest Pet of Them All

PERHAPS THE MOST BIZARRE association between man and beast is that of man and elephant. It is seldom realized that these creatures have been the constant associates of men for millennia. They have played a leading role in the civilization of a substantial part of all humanity. At least four quite different kinds of elephants have evolved, two of them now extinct. Their association with man goes back to the Stone Age. What is more, elephants have never been truly domesticated, for they have never bred reliably in complete captivity. Although perhaps the tamest and most reliable of all "pets", almost all domesticated elephants have been trained after being caught in the wilds.

Tens, perhaps even hundreds of millennia ago, men lived in close and daily association with a number of different kinds of elephants—the African loxodont; the Indian or Asiatic elephant of South Asia; the woolly mammoth of Europe, central North-east Asia and North America; and the mastodons of North and Central America. Man hunted the elephant for food, and probably for its skin and ivory. In very early times the true elephant of South Asia appears to have been caught and used as a work animal and for war. It seems to have been fully domesticated.

There are those who would hardly regard an elephant as a pet; they would be very wrong indeed. This enormous beast, once it accepts the

(above)
For thousands of years, man has used the **Indian** or **Asiatic elephant** as a giant beast of burden. It does not breed well in captivity, however, so each new generation must be captured and tamed from the wild. Once tame, it is among the most reliable of pets. Unfortunately, both African and Asiatic species are becoming increasingly rare.

(right)
Possibly the most intelligent nonhuman animals, **dolphins** have a highly developed language that we are now trying to translate. They have befriended people on many occasions since ancient times, been trained to perform in large seaquariums, played with children in the water and driven sharks away from life rafts. This **Amazonian dolphin** is one of the river dolphins.

idea that it is no longer wild but an associate of man, is gentle as well as useful. An elephant, if properly fed, is the healthiest of animals, but a full-grown elephant requires some seven hundred pounds of feed a day, and the present price of alfalfa hay makes it, in western countries, perhaps the most expensive of all animals to provide for.

Aquatic Mammals Are Among the Most Intelligent of Pets

SINCE ANCIENT TIMES there has been a belief that dolphins and teenage boys make wonderful playmates. The belief appeared in Roman legend, and Pliny, that master writer of fiction and fact, devoted many pages to the most wondrous description of boys who rode dolphins across bays to school, and of a dolphin that was a pet at a seaside resort in North Africa and liked music! Until recently these stories were thought to be pure myth; but now dolphins have been tamed in several large seaquaria. There are authentic records of boys riding on and playing with dolphins off beaches, and there are films and hundreds of photographs to prove this. These come from Europe, Australia, New Zealand and North America. Dolphins appear to be very intelligent and their playfulness is genuine. In fact, it is an expression of good spirits—just as it is in young boys.

Birds that Talk Like People

ALTHOUGH LARGE NUMBERS of birds are customarily kept as pets, there are only three families which can become truly domesticated. These are the parrots, starlings and crows. Strangely, all have the ability to imitate the human voice with varying degrees of success. Some, like the budgerigar, the mynah and the raven, can do so with unnerving accuracy.

The parrots represent an enormous natural group or family, members

(bottom left)
There are 315 clearly defined species of **parrots,** a distinctive, ancient order in which there are more tamed species than there are in any other group of birds. Parrots are intelligent, and their ability to "talk" by imitating human speech is well known. Their range includes most tropical regions, especially South America and Australasia.

(bottom right)
The shape and structure of a parrot's beak are illustrated in a view of the parrot's skull (1); note that the top part of the beak is separately hinged to the upper jaw, an arrangement that permits greater flexibility. A parrot's foot (2) has two toes pointing forward, one backward, and a fourth that can be moved either way. By contrast, the foot of a climbing bird (3) has four sharp-clawed toes whose relative positions are fixed.

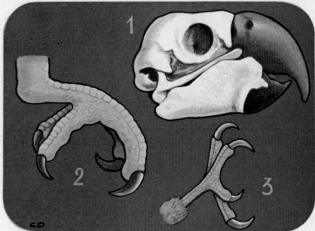

(top left)
Lorikeets of Oceania use their brushlike tongues to lick succulent juices from fruits and flowers.

(top right)
Cockatoos, native to Australasia, can erect the feathers of their brightly colored crests. They eat grain as well as nuts and fruit and often flock to plunder crops.

(above, left)
Owl-like in appearance, the New Zealand **kakapo** is a nocturnal ground dweller that nests in hollow places among tree roots and heavy vegetation. It is very close to extinction.

(above, right)
Largest members of the parrot family, the colorful long-tailed **macaws** inhabit the tropical forests of the Americas. They have been kept as pets for centuries, but some species have become extinct.

of which are spread over Australia, tropical Asia, Africa, Central and South America, with some inhabiting New Zealand and the Pacific Islands. They are even more numerous and varied than the pigeons, totalling no less than 315 clearly defined species. They are a distinctive ancient group placed in an order by themselves, *Psittaciformes*. Probably more species of parrots have been raised in captivity than any other group of birds.

Parrots have hinged, movable upper beaks and short truncated lower beaks on the normally-hinged lower jaw. Another unusual feature of parrots is their toe arrangement; one toe points permanently backward, but another may be moved either way so that they can have three pointing forward and one backward, or two pointing each way. They are the only birds that can pick up their food in one foot and bring it up to their mouths; this enables them to feed and watch out for enemies at the same time. Although parrots are intelligent birds, their ability to produce recognizable speech sounds, and even phrases, is purely imitative.

The real headquarters of the tribe is Australia and the Indo-Malayan region, but there are almost as many kinds in tropical America. Actually, the parrots may be divided into two lots, one of which contains the lories of Australasia and the Pacific, and the strange, carnivorous keas and the kakas of New Zealand and surrounding islands. The other group contains a single, rather mysterious ground-living type including the kakapo of New Zealand, the cockatoos of Australia and the parrots, parakeets, lovebirds, budgerigars, lorikeets, cockatiels and macaws. Specimens of most of the known forms have been kept as pets at one time or another. Apart from the keas, kakapos and certain nocturnal Australian species, all have many characteristics in common, from the little grass parakeets of Australia to the huge macaws of the Amazon. Above all, the plumage of most varieties is brilliantly pigmented.

Not all parrots "talk". There are several that apparently are incapable of imitating speech, and only exceptional individuals of most other species ever do acquire the art. The best "talker" is the West African grey parrot and the next, perhaps, is the Panamanian yellow-browed.

There Are Many Kinds of "Blackbirds"

THE STARLINGS FORM a large group of medium-sized birds with headquarters in India and the Oriental region. One member of the family, the mynah, has become increasingly popular as a pet. These are talking birds, but are not related to the parrots. The two best talkers are the Javan mynah, found in Malaya, Java and the Sunda Islands; and the greater Indian hill mynah, ranging from northern India to Vietnam. The mynahs are considered the most talkative of all birds.

In Eurasia, the raven, crow and jackdaw have been kept as pets for hundreds of years. These are pure black, the largest being the raven with a beautiful spreading "bib" on his chest, and the smallest, the jackdaw. Jays and magpies have also been caged as pets.

Ravens and crows can readily be taught to talk; jackdaws will occasionally master a few words, but the magpies and jays apparently

If tamed when young, both ravens and crows make intelligent "talking" pets. The raven is the largest of the pure black starlings, attaining a length of two feet or more. Although not harmful to crops—as are crows—it has been vigorously hunted and has become rare in many areas. Crows, on the other hand, seem to be growing more numerous despite persecution and the spread of cities. Pictured here are the **carrion crow** (bottom left), which closely resembles the raven, and the **hooded crow** (bottom right), a subspecies of the carrion crow.

cannot do so, though they can make noises very much like human speech. All have the habit of collecting bright shiny objects and hiding them in unlikely places. The jackdaw is the master thief of all. Many stories about its thievery may be found in German, French and English literature.

Some farmers consider the crow a pest. Ravens, however, do no damage to crops and can do much good as "waste-disposal units". Unfortunately, many farmers have never considered the bird in this light and the raven has been mercilessly persecuted all over the world. As a result, this bird is now rare in many places and should be carefully protected.

Many authorities proclaim birds of the genus *Corvus* to be the most highly developed of the birds. The sly and wily American crow has such a reputation, and is one of those few creatures whose numbers continue to increase in spite of constant persecution and increasing urbanization.

Pigeons and Doves Are Widely Dispersed

ANOTHER GROUP OF BIRDS that have played a tremendous role in the history of man are the pigeons. They form one of the largest natural groups or families of birds and are spread all over the land surfaces of the earth. They range in size from the great crowned gouras of the Pacific, almost as big as turkeys, to tiny ground-living doves about the size of sparrows. Many species have been kept as pets and many more have proven popular as zoo animals. Two species were fully domesticated in ancient times—the little long-tailed doves originally inhabiting the Mediterranean and Middle Eastern countries, from which sundry pale-tinted and pure white breeds have been developed, and the short-tailed rock dove (or common pigeon) of Europe, from which all domestic breeds of pigeons have been derived.

The remarkable, but of course by no means unique, "homing" power of pigeons was early noticed by man, and there is evidence that the Egyptians, Cretans and Greeks used the bird to carry messages. Pigeons subsequently played a very important role as couriers in war. They are so employed even today.

An interesting domesticated South American bird is known as the chunga bird. It is one of the most intelligent, faithful and courageous of all pets. Known only to some Argentinian, Brazilian and Uruguayan landowners, it is a delicate bird with long black legs and beautiful pale grey plumage. The chunga bird stands eighteen inches to two feet tall, and has a wide, somewhat hooked bill. Actually there are two closely related kinds of birds known variously as the seriema, or crested screamer; and the chunia or chunga respectively. The latter inhabits the Argentine bush areas and nests in trees. Both have been domesticated since pre-Columbian times and today are kept on many farmsteads to protect chickens from marauding dogs and wild animals.

There is no scientific distinction between **doves** and **pigeons,** but most people call the smaller varieties doves. Gentle birds, they are easily domesticated and are popular pets in many parts of the world. Homing pigeons have long been used to carry news or messages.

Llamas are strong and able to work at heights of 15,000 feet, where the thin oxygen would seriously weaken horses or oxen. Even today, they are used to carry ore from mines high in the Andes Mountains. The Incas had domesticated the llama long before the invasion by the Spanish conquistadores.

Chunga birds are absolutely fearless, and because they eat small mammals, lizards and insects, they serve as a good check on these animals.

The Longest and Skinniest of All

PROBABLY NO CREATURES have played a greater part in myth and folklore than snakes and, despite what many people may think, none is more "popular" in certain respects.

The keeping of snakes as pets is a great deal more prevalent than most of us would suppose. There is a brisk national and international trade and tens of thousands of these reptiles serve as pets in American and European homes. The keeping of snakes as pets, especially by youngsters, is not recommended, because without some rather specialized knowledge and a lot of patience, the reptiles can easily be either starved to death or overfed.

Snakes are extremely numerous and varied. There are "flying snakes" that actually glide from tree to tree in Indonesia; deadly poisonous sea snakes which sometimes congregate in unbelievable numbers on the surface of the warm oceans; burrowing snakes; jumping snakes; and sidewinders. The subject of snakes is a vast one and is not really in our province, except to note that an astonishing number are kept as pets. Moreover, there is one type that has almost become domesticated. This is the boa-constrictor of tropical America. The pythons of Africa and the Orient are also well on the way to the same status due to their similar habits. This is a peculiar business which usually mystifies city dwellers. It should be remembered that in the tropics houses are almost always raised on pillars or pilings to prevent dampness and rot as well as to provide ventilation from below. In such countries rats are extremely

Boas (in tropical America) and pythons (in Africa and Asia) are encouraged to live under houses, where they hunt rodents. They become amiable, though not affectionate, pets and are noted for their gentleness, size and color patterns.

(top left)
Like the cow, the common domestic fowl, or **chicken,** has no wild ancestors and depends on man for survival. Baby chicks, like baby ducks, are popular gift pets and, along with baby turtles and anoles ("baby chameleons"), are given as prizes at carnivals. No animal should be a gift or a prize, however, because unless a long-term commitment is made for its care, it very soon dies.

(top right)
Rabbits multiply rapidly and are easy to house and feed. They are familiar pets and have been raised for a long time for their flesh and fur. All domesticated rabbits were developed from the European wild rabbit, and they will revert to wild coloration and smaller size a few generations after escaping from capitivity.

prevalent. Boas and pythons very often take up residence under the houses where they perform an excellent service by keeping down the numbers of rodents.

Some Pets Are Amphibious

ONE OF THE ODDEST MEMBERS of this group is a creature known as the axolotl. This is actually the larval form—pure white, with large feathery gills—of a species of Mexican salamander related to the tiger salamander. The axolotl becomes sexually mature while still in the larval form. Some species may never change from the larval body form but they are still able to reproduce. Apparently these creatures were kept in ornamental pools by the Aztecs, and specimens were brought to Europe and North America at an early date, where they were placed on display in fishbowls. They measure up to ten inches in length, float and are not at all attractive, but for some reason they became popular as pets. It was not until comparatively recent times that these animals were discovered to be the arrested larval forms of the big black, gold, yellow, red and white spotted salamanders. The Aztecs, however, knew this and kept the animals because they considered them to be immortal symbols of longevity and possibly of youth.

Man Even Keeps Insects and Arachnids

COCKROACHES ARE MAINTAINED in many Oriental countries but are considered Chinese specialties. These insects are well cared for and trained to fight—for man's entertainment.

Another extraordinary custom has been practised in West Africa for centuries. Itinerant magicians from the northern and drier areas journey through the southern forested countries, giving performances of magic. Among these performers are certain men who capture and tame large scorpions and keep them living inside their clothes. From these the poisonous tail-spine has not been removed. Yet these potentially dangerous creatures wander about on these men, even while they sleep on the open ground; they never sting them and never run away. They are truly pets and seem to respond to commands given to them by a touch of their owner's finger.

Spur-of-the-Moment Buying Is Usually Unwise

AT EASTER TIME in some countries children are given baby chickens, baby ducks, or young white rabbits as pets. Anoles, erroneously called chameleons, are often purchased at pet shops, and tiny turtles with their shells brilliantly painted (a horror in itself) are available throughout the year. In nearly every instance these poor helpless creatures are the victims of impulsive buying, and almost invariably die a lingering and needless death from starvation, cold or rough handling stemming from ignorance. The owners of such "pets", bought without any rational desire, rarely take the time or trouble to educate themselves concerning the basic needs of the new animal. The practice of selling living creatures in this way is something to deplore and should be prevented.

However, the person who has an earnest desire for a pet and takes the time to assimilate pertinent facts regarding its selection, care, maintenance and welfare, enters into a meaningful relationship that will provide the creature with security and contentment, and one that will enrich the owner's life.

Macaws are among the most sought after parrots, for they not only repeat words but can "parrot" a whole sentence. Native to the Amazon region, these large parrots are characterized by brilliant plumage of bright, contrasting colors.

GOLIAT

► *The different breeds of dogs that have developed after countless centuries of change and evolution.*

Dogs

N OBODY KNOWS WHEN THE DOG first appeared on earth as a distinct type of animal, but it must have been a very long time ago indeed. Drawings found in Egyptian royal tombs at least 5,000 years old show that dogs of several sorts were used for hunting when the old monarchs for whom the tombs were erected were still alive; and there is reason to believe that long before this, as long as 20,000 years ago, the dog was already associated with man's dwelling places. And perhaps as much as 50,000 years in the past, man made use of a dog (or a "pre-dog") in hunting; even as today, the animal's senses were more acute and they were better than man at finding game.

Many people think that dogs are descended from wolves or foxes. Leading authorities, however, do not believe this. They point out that puppies resulting from the mating of dogs with either a wolf or a fox are unable to breed *with each other,* although they can breed with the stock of either parent. Consequently there is no way for a new, truly doglike animal to evolve from such crosses. On the other hand, any dog can be mated with any other dog, and their puppies *will* be able to breed among themselves.

All dogs are probably descended from unknown ancestors that were neither foxes nor wolves as we know these two animals today. Dogs undoubtedly are descended primarily from jackals and primitive wolves. The notably wolflike breeds are associated with the world's northern regions, and it seems likely that they resulted from the crossing of primitive man's jackal-dogs with the wolves he met in his early wander-

For many thousands of years, dogs have been associated with man, who has used them for hunting, transportation, protection and, of course, companionship. Although many dogs are wolflike in appearance, experts believe that they did not descend directly from wolves. However, crossbreeding with wolves, foxes and other doglike animals has occurred. When a dog is bred with a **coyote** (photo, top right), the resulting pet is called a "coy-dog."

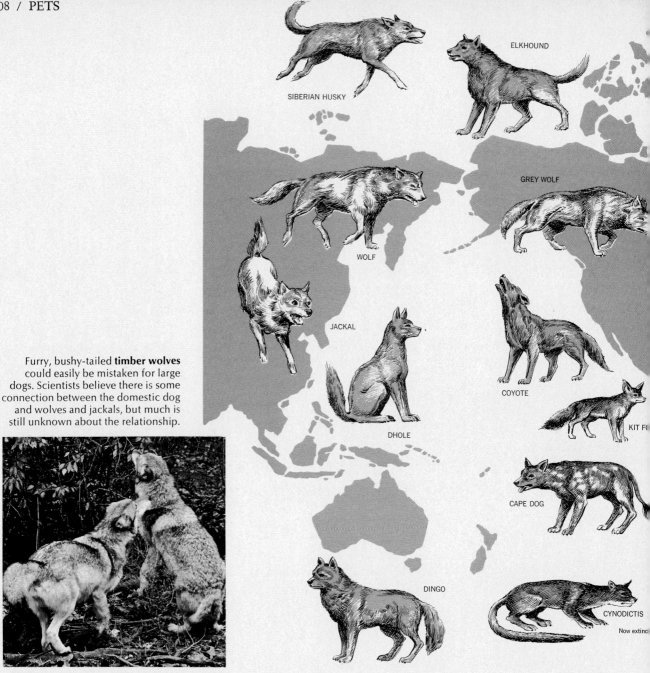

SIBERIAN HUSKY

ELKHOUND

GREY WOLF

WOLF

JACKAL

DHOLE

COYOTE

KIT FO

CAPE DOG

DINGO

CYNODICTIS
Now extinc

Furry, bushy-tailed **timber wolves** could easily be mistaken for large dogs. Scientists believe there is some connection between the domestic dog and wolves and jackals, but much is still unknown about the relationship.

ings around the globe. Thousands of years later, when a number of recognizable breeds had evolved, we begin to find mention of the dogs and their relations with man. The records in ancient Egyptian tombs indicate the existence of several distinct and well-established dog types. One was lightly built, apparently a hunter that depended on speed and good eyesight, as does the greyhound. Others were much heavier and more powerful, with short coats and massive heads. And a third,

WOLF

GREY FOX

RED FOX

IBIZAN HOUND

JACKAL

BIG-EARED FOX

HYENA

Wild members of the dog family are found all over the world, often roaming in packs as did their primitive ancestors. Some of these wild breeds or species have been tamed by man in many parts of the globe. The Siberian husky is a pet in Asia, and coyotes have been tamed in the United States. An ancient wild breed, the dingo, is trained for hunting by Australian aborigines.

which may have had its origin in some colder region, had erect "pricked" ears, a thick, furry coat, and a tail that curled almost flat on his back. The tails of foxes and wolves, on the other hand, usually droop behind them.

Two very early wild dog species still exist. They are the dhole, in India; and the dingo, in Australia. Both are reddish, with rounded ears that stand straight up, and rather long and slender jaws. They hunt in packs and are so much alike that they may have had the same ancestors, although they now live in regions more than 4,000 miles apart!

If it is really true that all dogs are descended from the same original stock, how has it happened that there are so many very different breeds today? Can the tiny Chihuahua possibly be related to the huge St. Bernard, or a fluffy little Pomeranian to a satin-smooth Great Dane who is almost big enough to hide it in his mouth? They can indeed— and the great variety in which dogs now exist is not by any means simply an accident of nature. Here is how such contrasts came about.

Men have kept dogs for all kinds of purposes of their own, for thousands of years. They have been used in hunting, and for guarding sheep or other domestic flocks; they have been used as beasts of burden, and as guardians of the home against wild animals and human intruders. These are only a few of the ways in which dogs have proved to be very useful indeed in the past—and in which they continue to be used by man today. Dogs have repaid these attentions by becoming real partners of their two-legged owners.

Naturally, in different parts of the world dogs have had different jobs to do for their masters. Some tasks have called for great size and strength, others for special characteristics such as agility or an especially acute sense of smell. So, as time passed, people in different parts of the world naturally kept those puppies which happened to be best suited to their particular purposes, and used them as breeding-stock. By continuing such selection for many dog generations the desired qualities became stronger and appeared more frequently, because any animal tends to have offspring at least partly like itself. Little by little the differences between "breeds" became greater, and the foundations were laid for the many breeds that we have today.

As many as 115 definite breeds are recognized and listed by just one leading authority—the American Kennel Club. There is not room here to discuss them all; but we can discuss and describe a selection, chosen because they help to illustrate the great range of size, and the varied abilities to be found among these animals which have had a special relationship with man for so long. If your own preferred breed is not included, lack of space, not prejudice, is the reason!

A Dog That's Named After a Bird

T HE "MERRY LITTLE COCKER" is a very old breed. In fact, his ancestors can be traced almost as far back as the year 1400. He has always hunted birds, especially the woodcock, and he was so good at this that in time he became known as the "cocking spaniel", or just plain "cocker". These early instincts are still strong in him today, as many sportsmen can testify. But most of us think of the modern cocker spaniel principally as a first-class family dog, thoroughly at home under almost any conditions you can imagine.

Descended from the fifteenth-century spaniels of Spain, the **cocker spaniel** has large expressive eyes, long ears and a soft, wavy coat. It is handsome in any of numerous colors, from solid blacks, reds and beiges to combinations of black, tan and white.

Cocker spaniels show more variations in hue than almost any other breed. Solid blacks, reds, buffs and creams (the last two called "blonds") are frequent, as are black-and-whites and black-and-tans. A few are almost all white. And finally there are some varieties in which black, tan, and white are found in combination.

The soft, usually wavy, coat of this small and engaging dog is longest on the ears, chest, legs and underside of the body. His tail is naturally quite long, but breeders "dock" or shorten it almost to a stump when the puppies are only a few days old. This is an old custom which started, with good reason, when cockers were used chiefly for hunting. A cocker keeps his tail wagging while he is hunting. If it were long, this constant thrashing against brush and through briers would make it very sore, and it would pick up dozens of burrs.

Like their distant relatives, the English setters, cockers can "talk" with their eyes as well as with their voices. In fact, dogs in general and cockers in particular have quite a range of "facial expressions". Many of these can be recognized by anyone who spends a little time watching dogs closely, and animal behaviorists such as Dr. Konrad Lorenz have an almost uncanny ability of knowing what a dog is about to do, determined by the dog's "expression" and body posture.

General Manager of the Sheep Flocks

THE WORLD'S BEST-KNOWN SHEEP-HERDING DOG is the rough-coated collie. This breed has been known and used in Scotland for nearly three hundred years—but concerning its ancestry we know nothing, although it seems likely that they, too, had been herders in some part of the world.

To work effectively with a shepherd in controlling and protecting his flock calls for a high degree of canine intelligence. Sheep are not only easily frightened; they are often very stubborn. To keep them under control both man and dog must be firm and patient, and work perfectly together. A good collie seems to know this as well as his master does, and between them they can do a job of persuasion, guidance and control that seems scarcely possible even when one sees it demonstrated.

Collies of today are more streamlined than their ancestors. Their skulls are less broad, their muzzles are longer, and they tend to be taller than they once were. Despite these physical changes, they are still one of the most intelligent breeds and, when properly trained, perform beautifully.

The typical modern collie makes an ideal family dog, as do most traditional working breeds. Collies are good-tempered by nature, alert, and extremely devoted to their human friends. You can teach them almost anything that a dog can do, which is one of the reasons why they make such a good showing in the obedience training classes which are popular today.

A Specialist in Saving Lives

DIFFERENT DOG BREEDS have various claims to fame, but none of them can prove its case more completely than the giant St. Bernard of the Swiss Alps. For three centuries these dogs have been used by the monks of the hospice in the St. Bernard Pass as helpers in rescuing travellers lost in the snow. It is a matter not of conjecture, but of record, that, during this period, they have played an important part in saving some 2,500 lives. Forty of these rescues can be credited to the work of a single dog, Barry, the greatest of them all.

The first St. Bernards were brought to the old hospice as watchdogs about the year 1670. The monks there soon discovered that the animals' keen sense of smell, pathfinding ability and great strength enabled them to find foot-travellers who had become lost, and sometimes buried, in the mountain snowstorms. So they began to make it a routine matter to take these huge dogs with them on every lifesaving search. The dogs quickly learned the purpose of these expeditions, and it wasn't long before they were going out on patrol, *by themselves,* in groups

The majestic **collie** was originally only about fourteen inches high, but its size has been nearly doubled through careful breeding. A very intelligent dog, it has been used for centuries as a sheep-herder.

Amazing endurance and extremely sharp senses enable the **Saint Bernard** to find and rescue travelers lost in treacherous mountain snowstorms. Very gentle though of great size, the dog—according to legend—will allow the wayfarer to drink from the keg around its neck and will shield him from the cold with its warm fur.

of three or four. When a storm victim was found, two of the dogs would lie down beside him and provide warmth, while another would return to the hospice, alert the monks, and guide them back to the scene.

To aid him in this preliminary rescue work, each dog was equipped with a little cask of liquor hung from his neck for the benefit of any stranded wayfarer who needed it. When the rescuing monks arrived, all the dogs would realize that, with the exception of leading the whole party back to the hospice, their duty had been completed.

The present-day St. Bernard dog is believed to be a descendant of the heavy Molossus dogs of Asia, brought by the Roman legions into the country they knew as Helvetia nearly 2,000 years ago.

When bull-baiting and dog-fighting were popular "sports," the fierce-looking **boxer** was used to fight against bulls and against other dogs. When beginning to battle, the boxer will stand on its hind legs and paw vigorously with its front legs, in a true "boxing" fashion.

He Used to Be a Professional Fighter

ONE OF THE STRANGE FACTS about dogs is the way that the popularity of different breeds rises and falls; perhaps we should more accurately say that this is a strange fact about man. There is always some demand for every recognized breed; but as far as general public interest is concerned, no single breed ever remains the "number one breed" for very long. The case of the boxer is a good example of how a previously almost disregarded breed can strike sudden popularity.

Thirty years ago this husky, energetic and extremely capable smooth-coated canine was almost unknown outside Germany. But then he began to do some winning in important shows; this apparently started his spectacular rise to fame. Now it sometimes seems as though every third or fourth person you meet in the United States either has a boxer already or wants one—regardless of whether or not he has ever owned a dog of any kind before.

So far from being newcomers to the dog world, boxers come from a line that has been widely known in Europe since the sixteenth century. Even a quick glance at a boxer will show that he is not too distantly related to both the mastiff and the bulldog, although other breeds are doubtless included in his ancestry. The boxer gets his name from his habit of rearing up on his hind legs and pawing with the front legs. The dog does this both when starting to fight and when welcoming a friend.

Until about a century ago the boxer, like others of his general type, was used for such so-called sports as dog-fighting and bull-baiting; the idea of setting one or more dogs to do battle with a bull would appeal to few people nowadays as a "spectator sport", even if such gory pastimes were not forbidden by law. But it is easy to understand why a dog with such a background will be likely to have the necessary attributes for serving as a first-class defender of his owner's home and property. Even the boldest marauder might well hesitate to tangle with a full-grown boxer. In fact, this stout-hearted canine dynamo was one of the first breeds chosen for police training in his native Germany.

(top left)
Related to the wild dogs of northern regions, the **chow chow** has a blackish tongue and a thick coat for protection against cold temperatures. A native of China, it has been an effective hunter for centuries.

(top right)
The sleek and strong-jawed **borzoi,** or **Russian wolfhound,** is seen today in the United States mainly as a showdog; but this dog, whose name means "the swift one," was widely used in Russia for tracking and killing wolves.

Strange Dog of the Far East

WHEN YOU MEET A CHOW CHOW face to face you may wonder if he is actually a dog or some other kind of animal. His expression seems to be a strange combination of scowl, dignity and coolness; if he happens to yawn you will see that the inside of his mouth and even his tongue are almost black instead of the usual doggy pink!

As you get to know him better you will realize that he is a very real dog. He has been used successfully as a hunting dog in his native China for hundreds of years, and has an excellent record in hunting both wolves and bears; he can also be employed as a game dog, and points pheasants and other birds more or less as our Western pointers and setters do. One sport-loving Chinese Emperor who lived more than a thousand years ago kept a kennel of some 5,000 chow-type dogs and a huge staff of huntsmen to handle them.

There is little doubt that the chow's early ancestral history is closely connected with those of the Eskimo husky, Samoyed, Norwegian elkhound and other breeds of the Far North. All have the same general sort of heavy coat, stocky build, erect ears, and tail laid close along the back. But the chow chow is the only one of the group that has a noticeably short, "cobby" body and an almost black tongue. Some authorities declare that this dog from the Far East is one of the oldest recognizable types in the whole world of dogs.

Master of Speed and Winter Weather

EVEN A QUICK GLANCE at a typical borzoi shows that he is a tremendously strong fellow and built for great running speed. He usually measures about thirty inches tall at the shoulder and is likely to weigh ninety or one hundred pounds. His long, strong jaws look as though he could catch and hold almost any animal of his own size.

Remembering these things, it is easy to understand why borzois were known in the United States as Russian wolfhounds until twenty or thirty years ago. So far as domesticated dogs are concerned, they are probably the best in the world for running down and killing wolves, hares and other game. The Russian nobility used them for this purpose for at least two centuries, and they have proved equally successful in the western United States where they have been tested on wolves and coyotes.

Authorities on dogs believe that the borzoi originated from the crossing of native Russian dogs, looking somewhat like our modern collie, with imported Arabian greyhounds. The greyhounds, of course, had short, thin coats and could not stand the cold of northern winters. But their mating with the hardy native breed produced puppies who grew up to have much of the greyhounds' speed, and the heavier coat of the Russian dogs. By carefully selecting and breeding the most promising puppies from later litters, the borzoi became established as a type that could be relied on to "breed true".

It is unlikely that a dog as large and specialized as the borzoi will ever become very popular, and nowadays they are rarely seen except in the larger dog shows. But it is a breed well worth looking out for, because of its remarkable appearance, and as an example of how man can develop a dog type to fit special purposes and special conditions.

Great Guardian and Family Friend

THE GERMAN SHEPHERD'S NAME has a double meaning. He has been closely connected with Germany, where his ancestors herded livestock and guarded farms for many centuries before the present type of dog was developed. During all this time, the Alsatian hound, as he is known in Britain, has worked very closely with man, and because of this association and the constant efforts which have been made to improve him, his reputation for courage, brains, strength and devotion to his owner has spread throughout the world.

A breed with a family history such as this can be trained to do a whole variety of things, so it is not surprising that the German shepherd has been a tremendous success as a professional police dog in small towns and in large cities. He is one of the best breeds for "seeing eye" work, too: guiding blind owners around the streets, through traffic, into and out of office buildings and homes, and almost anywhere else they want to go. When properly trained, the German shepherd carries out such duties a good deal more intelligently than would many human beings confronted with the same problems.

A first-class shepherd is so perfectly built that when he walks or trots he seems to glide along without effort. And when he runs or leaps, it is quite an impressive sight. A full-grown male in proper condition should weigh about eighty pounds. He wears a double coat, with a dense, woolly lining next to the skin, covered with much coarser hair of about four or five inches in length. It is no wonder that he can endure the coldest and stormiest weather.

Today's **German shepherd** exhibits a high degree of intelligence in the many tasks man has trained it for. Strong and devoted, it is an accomplished police dog and "seeing eye" dog, among many other things.

The Carpenters Started This Pup

THERE IS LITTLE about the appearance of a Bedlington terrier to suggest that he was at one time noted in Britain as a fighting dog that was used as a killer of animals ranging from badgers to rats and mice. Yet such were typically his activities in the mining region around Bedlington, in Northumberland, where he originated more than a hundred years ago. He never went about looking for a fight, but if he got into one, he would stay to the end.

Early owners of the Bedlington were mostly carpenters; but the dogs earned such fame that wealthy Englishmen became interested and finally formed a special club and began to enter them in dog shows about the year 1880. Today, you can be sure to find several Bedlingtons on the benches in any important dog shows. They may look less rough-and-ready than the early specimens, but in size and general appearance they have hardly changed.

Bedlington terriers differ from other English breeds in several ways. In Bedlingtons, the line of the skull from just above the eyes to the tip of the nose is straight. In other breeds, there is a dip just forward of the eyes, and its lack in the Bedlington gives the breed an appearance that is unique. Nearly all other British terriers have stiff, rather wiry hair, but the Bedlington's is so soft and thick that it is almost wool. Before it became the custom to trim off most of it, the Bedlington wore a regular topknot of this fuzzy hair! There is certainly no other terrier which gallops with a movement so like a greyhound's.

A Hunter Everyone Loves

THE SMALLEST OF WHAT WE CALL the true hounds are short-coated, long-eared dogs which naturally hunt such animals as foxes, raccoon, hares and rabbits. They will follow their quarry's trail for hours,

(bottom left)
Distinctive in several ways, **Bedlington terriers** have a "straight-line" facial profile, enormous speed, and a coat unlike those of other British terriers. Instead of wiry rough hair, the Bedlington, although short-haired, has a thick wooly coat that is soft to the touch.

(bottom right)
Developed in Germany, the **dachshund** was first used for tracking badgers and then for hunting larger animals, such as the wild boar.

(left)
Colorful red jackets and a pack of **beagles** mean the beginning of a hunt for these members of a hunt club. The beagles, leaders of the chase, are followed by the riders, who listen for the dogs' long howling barks as the hunt progresses.

(below)
Built stockily and close to the ground, the **basset hound** excels at hunting. Its mournful look, floppy ears and loose skin are characteristic. Long a fine hunter in Europe, it has become popular in the United States.

often uttering long-drawn-out, almost musical barks or howls. Their noses are always close to the ground when hunting, for they depend entirely on their remarkably keen sense of smell to tell them which way the game has gone. And most of the time their tails are wagging fast and high.

Beagles and other hounds of this general type hunt well in couples and even in packs of twenty or more, much as the dhole and dingo which were mentioned earlier have the habit of doing.

Hunting rabbits and hares with beagle packs has been a popular sport in England and the United States for a long time. Hunt clubs and "beagling" clubs have been formed in many areas, and their members often wear special uniforms. They follow the dogs either on foot or on horseback, and when a fox or hare is started there is sure to be a wild chase trying to keep up with the pack.

The beagle's love of hunting is only part of his character. He is naturally good-tempered, healthy, friendly, devoted and easy to care for. In recent years he has become popular as a regular member of the family, for, if you have any liking at all for dogs, the beagle is sure to win you over. Only twelve to fifteen inches tall at the shoulder, he is small enough to be convenient indoors, or in a car, and is inexpensive to feed.

At first glance a basset hound appears to be somewhat like a large, short-legged beagle. A closer examination reveals that the basset's height and weight are only slightly greater than the beagle's, but his body is much longer. These dogs have descended from ancient French bloodlines, and were widely used in badger hunts as long ago as the 1500s. It was not until 1875, however, that the breed reached England, where it won immediate popularity. They have been found in the United States for many years, and the breed has recently become much in demand. Registrations increased sixty-eight per cent *in a single year*— apparently as a direct result of a basset hound having a star role in a television series! This breed makes a very good hunting dog, being slow enough for humans to follow easily. That its head looks much like a bloodhound's is not an accident—the two share a common ancestry. Bassets have engaging and endearing personalities; their owners are devoted to them.

From Circus Tent to Sporting Dog

I F YOU ARE INTERESTED in a big, cheerful and kindly sort of dog that likes to be with people and is naturally well-behaved, one of the large retrievers may be the best choice. The most common are the Labrador, the Chesapeake Bay, and the golden retrievers. The Labrador, named for the peninsula, originated in Newfoundland; the Chesapeake resulted from the chance mating of a couple of shipwrecked New- foundland dogs with some Maryland dogs they found on reaching shore. The golden retriever, so the story goes, got its start when a Scot named Lord Tweedmouth was so impressed with a circus troupe of eight per- forming Russian dogs in Brighton, England, that he bought the lot. To reduce the breed's size, he crossed them with bloodhounds. The result was a happy one; the golden retriever has a very good nose, is hardy, retrieves all sorts of game, and can do dozens of other jobs equally well.

It is usually very easy to tell the common retrievers apart. The Chesapeake has a reddish-tan or "dead-grass" hue, and a curly coat. Golden retrievers have a shining golden coat, with lighter "feather- ings"; Labradors, as everyone knows, are black. The only complication arises because Labs are not always black. They may be yellow or golden, and look much like a golden retriever. If in doubt, look at the tail. A golden retriever has a well-feathered tail, rather like a setter's, while the Labrador's tail is stocky, smooth-haired and round in cross-section.

Retrievers are intelligent, and have big, broad heads with plenty of room for brains. They are completely loyal, thoroughly dependable, and come as close to having "reasoning power" as any dog alive. They swim readily and nonchalantly, even when they have to shoulder ice floes aside to make their way. Their heavy, oily coat keeps the skin warm and almost dry. Indoors, however, this same oiliness causes the dog to give off a heavy and not very welcome smell in an overheated room; but this should rarely be a cause for complaint by its owner because the breed has a natural preference for fairly cool surroundings. And it would be hard to find a more useful and faithful canine friend than any one of the retrievers.

Gallant Gentleman and Friend

O F THE THREE COMMON KINDS OF SETTERS (English, Gordon and Irish) the Irish is the one that most people know best because of the beauty of his glistening mahogany-red coat, and his wonderful

While most **Labrador retrievers** are black, some, like this one, are yellow or golden. They may be distinguished from golden retrievers by their stocky, smooth-haired tails.

(left)
A glistening red-brown coat makes the **Irish setter,** originally a bird hunter, a prized family dog. In the full-grown adult, the lush "feathering" of the tail, underside and chest adds much to its beauty.

(below)
Belonging to the terrier group, **schnauzers** have been bred to three recognized sizes: giant, standard and miniature. Thriving on plenty of exercise, all three are better suited to country fields than to city streets.

disposition. He is bright, lively, and always ready for action. He likes people and is one of the handsomest breeds in any show. No wonder he has made a hit as a family dog, particularly in country homes where there is plenty of room for the outdoor exercise which means so much to him.

The Irish setter, like his cousins the black-and-brown Gordon and the mostly white English, was first brought to the United States for employment in hunting as a "bird dog". He gave a good account of himself in this difficult work, but training him for it was sometimes rather difficult, for he often has such a strong will of his own that he gained the reputation of being wild and "hard-headed". As a gun dog, many sportsmen feel that "when he is good he is very, very good; but when he is bad he is horrid." Hence, he is now much less popular for this kind of work than the English setter and the pointer.

This, however, should not be held against him except in the hunting field! He is devoted to his master or mistress, and usually gets along splendidly with children. Although he is big, he is so well proportioned and graceful that he can move around in a crowded living room without getting in the way. And he is so gentlemanly and responsive to a word of praise and a pat on the head that unless you are very strong-minded he will soon own the entire household.

Small Dog with a Big Future

THERE ARE THREE DIFFERENT TYPES of schnauzers, all of which hail from Germany. The largest is the powerful, heavy-set giant schnauzer, as much as twenty-five inches tall at the shoulder. Next comes the standard breed, about six inches less in shoulder height, and finally the miniature, who resembles a standard except for his much smaller size. His growing army of friends call him the "Mini", and hail him as the brainiest and best of all the smallish terriers.

(top)
The **poodle** is not of French origin, as many people believe, although it has long been a favorite pet in France. This curly-haired dog, which comes in many shades, was probably developed long ago in Germany. Today it is popular in many countries.

(above)
Papillon means "butterfly" in French, a descriptive name for this good-looking dog with its erect wing-shaped ears. Many famous people have chosen the papillon as a pet, probably because of its graceful, plumed tail and luxuriant coat, as well as for its affectionate nature.

This strongly built, agile little dog fully deserves his reputation for high spirits, courage, good sense, and complete devotion to the people with whom he lives. He usually shows a particular preference for some one person, but not so exclusively that you would call him a "one-man" dog. "One-family" is a better description of him, and no other breed lives up to it better than he does.

"Minis" are second to none as alarm-giving watchdogs. Their sense of hearing is extremely sharp, and they catch the faintest sound so quickly that you often think that they sleep with both ears on the alert. When they think that something is wrong they sound off and investigate immediately. But they are not "yappy" dogs and, under customary conditions, are rather quiet.

Miniature schnauzers are even-tempered with children as well as grown-ups, and seldom wander around the neighborhood to any extent. Although they have plenty of courage and self-respect, they are not inclined to be quarrelsome with other dogs. The general rule that strong, active dogs deserve country rather than city life certainly applies to all the schnauzers. They can take a terrific amount of outdoor exercise and enjoy every step of it.

Which Size Do You Like Best?

FOR MANY YEARS the poodle has been the world's most famous performing circus dog. He has been taught to do many difficult tricks which you would think were beyond the abilities of any "mere dog". In the old days the best performers attracted crowds wherever they appeared. Naturally, only the brightest ones could do the extra-special stunts, and so there was a great demand for their puppies, which could be expected to inherit at least some of their ability. The result was that, as time went on, the breed's natural intelligence became still greater.

Years ago, these quick-witted dogs were known as French poodles, simply because they were particularly popular in France. Nobody really knows where they came from originally, but it is quite likely that they were developed in Germany. One of their important uses there was to retrieve ducks and other game birds which fell in the water after being shot.

Poodles, like schnauzers, come in three sizes: standard, miniature, and toy. The standard poodles measure fifteen or more inches high at the shoulder; miniatures are from a little over ten to almost fifteen inches, and toy poodles are ten inches or less. A purebred poodle may be solid white, brown, grey, bluish or black. There is even a peculiar shade which the breeders call "pink".

Whatever its size, a poodle usually makes a splendid companion dog. He is particularly satisfactory when he has been given regular training, for he loves to put his keen mind to work. Once started, he learns rapidly, and there is almost no limit to the accomplishments the poodle can master with the help of a good teacher, for he is a hardier dog than you might think, and as agile as a rubber ball in both body and spirit.

It seems that man has always been attracted to miniatures, and dogs are no exception. "Toy" dogs have been bred and regarded as objects of pride by wealthy or aristocratic owners for many centuries. In Europe, there are many records of the "toy continental spaniel". That the breed has managed to survive the almost helter-skelter cross-breedings which have sometimes been carried out in efforts to further reduce the dog's size is an indication that it became a true breed centuries ago. The present-day papillon is a direct descendant of the toy continental spaniel.

The papillon (which is French for "butterfly") or its ancestors appears in paintings and church frescoes dating from as far back as the thirteenth century. A number of Titian's paintings include a small dog very similar to the modern papillon. The dogs were carefully bred to produce fineness of bone and other features deemed desirable, and became steadily ever more popular, especially among the aristocracy of France and the Low Countries. Louis XIV loved these little dogs, and created the office of Valet de Chambre to care for them. Madame Pompadour owned two, and Marie Antoinette is supposed to have carried one with her on the ride to the guillotine. Many of the most famous artists of the past, including Rubens, Van Dyke and Goya, portrayed these dogs in their pictures.

It was not until the twentieth century that papillons came to England and the United States, but they made up for a late start by immediately discovering friends wherever they appeared. Few dogs have a more engaging "personality" or more enjoy human company than do papillons. They need little in the way of care, and are equally at home chasing rabbits through fields or living in city apartments. They stand about ten to eleven inches at the withers and are either two-toned or triple-toned. Common shades are white, black, sable and light or dark reddish-brown. Deceptively, the papillon looks small-headed because of the short hair on the head, and the beautiful long, fluffy coat of the

(bottom left)
A popular pet, the diminutive **Pekingese** stands only eight inches high at the shoulder. Its hair is fine and silky, and its full tail arches gracefully.

(bottom right)
It has been the fashion to shear **poodles** so that parts of their bodies are hairless and smooth, leaving their natural, tightly curled hair on other parts. Then they have a curly head of hair, furry "leggings" and a pom-pom tail.

GREYHOUND

SPRINGER SPANIEL

ENGLISH SETTER

IRISH TERRIER

SKYE TERRIER

DOBERMAN PINSCHER

DACHSHUND

The many species of dogs vary considerably in size, body form, and coat. For example, a dachshund could almost fit underneath a Saint Bernard; a slender greyhound could hardly be mistaken for a stocky chow; and with shaggy hair that even falls over its eyes, a Skye terrier has quite a different coat from its cousin, the short-haired Boston terrier.

body, which terminates in a flamboyantly plumed tail. It has been said the papillon "pulls at one's heartstrings", although not everyone would phrase it this way; but certainly there are few creatures in the world that make friends any faster with children and adults alike.

Six Names for a Fine Fellow

No other breed can boast of as many names as this large dog with the jet black or sometimes brown spots scattered over his short,

COCKER SPANIEL

GOLDEN RETRIEVER

FOXHOUND

CHOW

BOSTON TERRIER

SAINT BERNARD

Probably a mixture of several breeds, this working sled dog is well equipped with a heavy coat for the cold climate in which it lives. Judging from its build, it is likely that one of its parents was a Siberian husky.

glistening white coat. In one place or another he has been called English coach dog, carriage dog, firehouse dog, plum pudding dog, and spotted dick. His "real" name is Dalmatian, because Dalmatia is the country where he first became known much as we see him today.

Dalmatians have been used for a wide variety of purposes during their long history. We think of them first as followers and guardians of horse-drawn vehicles such as coaches, carriages—and especially fire engines —before those ponderous inventions were motorized and lost much of their old excitement. But a fair list of the other trades in which they

(right)
Very low-slung and almost waddling when they walk, **dachshunds** can be amazingly quick hunters out in the fields. Most dachshunds popular today are of the smooth-coated variety, but these dogs may also have wiry hair or long, fluffy coats, as does this one.

(below)
The dark-spotted **Dalmatian** has long been associated with coaches and fire engines, particularly horse-drawn types. No one knows why, but Dalmatians and horses get along beautifully, often becoming fast friends.

have made good would have to include livestock herding, following trails like a hound, retrieving, stag hunting, killing rats, pulling small carts, serving as guard dogs in wartime—and performing on the stage.

Any breed that can make a success of all these activities must have plenty of intelligence, good health, strength, speed and willingness to obey. No wonder then that the Dalmatian has become such a popular family companion. He is easy to take care of, too; for he is naturally clean, and his tight coat never needs trimming or combing. You might think that he would suffer from winter cold, but he doesn't seem to. Perhaps this is because his ancestors were outdoors in all kinds of weather for so many generations that temperature simply made no difference to them.

Possibly the strangest thing about a Dalmatian is his strong feeling of friendship toward horses, and of horses toward him. These two animals, oddly enough, seem to understand each other perfectly and often become inseparable companions.

What Will He Do Next?

YOU MIGHT NEVER GUESS that in their native Germany these amusing little characters have a well-earned reputation for routing badgers and foxes from their underground burrows, as well as for trailing deer and other game. But watch a dachshund out in the fields or woods and you will notice at once that he is a surprisingly fast runner and is always looking for something to catch or chase. In other words, they are born hunters as well as first-class dogs around the house.

The dachshund has been jokingly but rather accurately described as "half a dog high, a dog and a half long, and three dogs in the matter of brains." They are extremely strong for their weight, and their short legs, powerful front feet and long, "punishing" jaws are perfectly suited to battling an enemy underground. Yet a "dachsie" is seldom quarrelsome with other dogs, and under most circumstances is a friendly and cheerful companion.

Besides the things you teach them, dachshunds often develop amusing tricks and habits of their own. I knew one that lived on a large country place and loved to play with the kittens of the barn cats. Often, when we were sitting on the veranda, he would trot down the long driveway to the stables and return in a few minutes carrying a small kitten very carefully in his mouth. When he had laid it gently on the porch floor the two of them would scamper and play and have a wonderful time. Finally "Bandy", as we called him, would pick up his playmate and carry it quietly back to its mother, who never seemed to worry about the little one as long as the dog was baby-sitting.

Funny Face and Former Fighter

AS YOU WATCH A PUREBRED BULLDOG as he moves around a show ring it is hard to realize that at one time this breed was among the toughest of all dogs. That was in England two or more centuries ago, when bulldogs were bred and used chiefly for the "sports" of dog-fighting and battling with ugly-tempered bulls. Only the most fearless animals could succeed in such work. It is said that the bulldogs of those days were so savage that apparently they hardly felt the pain of the injuries they received.

How very different the modern bulldog is from those bloodthirsty ancestors! His tremendously powerful muzzle, head, neck and shoulders still show evidence of his former business, but his disposition has certainly changed. The love of fighting has just about disappeared, and "cruelty" seems to be far from his nature.

A good bulldog nowadays is an even-tempered animal with a shuffling, rolling sort of gait that makes you think of the walk of an old sailor, unused to dry land. A full-grown male weighs about fifty pounds and a female somewhat less. The coat may be brindle, solid white, red, fawn, or mixtures of any of these. And the more heavily wrinkled the face, head and throat, the more chance there is of being awarded a prize at the dog show.

(bottom left)
With smooth short hair and irregular spots, the coat of this **Great Dane** looks somewhat like that of the Dalmatian. The Dane, though, is much larger, with ears that are short and erect, unlike the Dalmatian's floppy black ears.

(bottom right)
The thick, powerfully built torso of the **bulldog** recalls this dog's early work of fighting against mean bulls. However, savagery has been bred out of this dog, which is today rather placid in nature.

The Canine Gamekeeper

BACK IN THE NINETEENTH CENTURY the life of a gamekeeper on a big English estate was a far from safe one. It was his job to keep his employer's great fields and woodlands well stocked with pheasants and other game, and to protect them from hungry enemies, including human poachers who would trap or shoot anything they could. Severe legal penalties for poaching were of no help unless the poacher was first caught!

What the gamekeepers needed were good dog assistants—powerful, fearless animals that would attack a poacher on command, then hold him down but not chew him too seriously. The men imagined that a breed that would be faster on its feet than the mastiff but larger and less savage than the bulldog would be fine for their purpose, so they began crossing bulldogs with mastiffs. The idea worked perfectly, and that was the start of the fine bull-mastiff guard dogs.

By the year 1900 the poaching situation was well under control. Meanwhile these crossbred dogs had attracted so much attention that many people wanted them as protectors for their homes. Experienced breeders began standardizing the gamekeepers' somewhat mongrelish animals and eliminating their "rough spots". More true mastiffs were used in the matings, and gradually standard characteristics were established. A large bull-mastiff of today weighs around 115 pounds, and is about sixty per cent mastiff and forty per cent bulldog. As for his disposition, a good bull-mastiff is fearless yet rather easily handled. He is alert, too, and without doubt one of the world's best watchdogs.

The Old English sheepdog is a breed whose name accurately describes both his origin and his specialty. That this long-coated dog has lived and worked in the west of England for many years is borne out by the appearance of one in a portrait dated 1770. The sheepdog was developed and used to drive sheep and cattle to market, and may also have been used to protect flocks from raids by sheep stealers. As a drover's dog he was tax-exempt, and his tail was docked to indicate his status. In some areas he was called "Bobtail".

Long woolly hair almost completely covering the eyes of the **Old English sheepdog** does not seem to keep this dog from its duties or from play. As its name implies, it was developed for driving sheep to market. When playing, it cavorts friskily and with surprising energy.

A statuesque breed, the **pointer** is a special help to hunters. Probably bred from the greyhound, bloodhound, and several other breeds, the pointer is first to pick up the scent of small game animals, "pointing" the way for the sportsman.

When a **pointer** catches the definite scent of a nearby bird, the dog "freezes" immediately, no matter how fast it has been running. Absolutely still, it stands like a stone figure, waiting for its master to reach the spot.

A sheepdog's coat is grey, or bluish-grey, with white markings, and so long and rich that it is almost like wool. In fact, combings furnish a first-class yarn for knitters. Although the dog's vision must be obstructed, this doesn't seem to hamper him very much. In fact, he bounds around playfully like a terrier. One cannot help but be amused at seeing one of these fifty-pound dogs cavorting like a puppy, crashing through bushes or throwing snow in all directions. The sheepdog has a peculiar rolling gait; at times he both looks and acts like a comic-strip animal. All his contours seem to be rounded, and if his head is turned away it may be difficult at first glance to tell which end is which! The comical, playful appearance belies a quick mind and a good deal of intelligence; the breed should not be regarded simply as a group of animated toys. Sheepdogs, with their hair clipped to provide better vision, served in the armed forces during World War II, and with their superb insulation against cold weather, they have been used as retrievers, sled dogs and watchdogs.

Bird Hunting Is His Trade

An excellent hunting dog, the **Tennessee Walker hound** is a strain of the American foxhound. It shares the intelligence, sharp nose, speed and stamina of the other hunting breeds.

MOST AUTHORITIES AGREE that the greyhound, foxhound, blood-hound, and a vanished breed known as the setting spaniel, all played a part in the origin of the splendid gun dog that we call the pointer. Probably he first appeared in Great Britain, even before fire-arms were invented, and in those early times his job was to find and "point" hares. Then the hunters would come up with their greyhounds, scare out the hare, and the chase would be on. He still finds and "points" game today—usually grouse and pheasant.

This "pointing" is a trait peculiar to a few breeds. It may start to operate when the dog's keen nose picks up a faint trace of the game's scent, either in the air or from a foot trail on the ground. If the pointer is uncertain where it comes from or how far away the bird is he will move cautiously this way and that, working closer and closer until his nose tells him the exact spot where the bird is hiding. Then he becomes as motionless as a statue. The hunter sees this, comes up behind the dog and either orders him forward or goes ahead himself and scares up the bird so that he can fire at it while it is on the wing.

It often happens that a pointer, zigzagging through a field at top speed as he hunts for a trace of game, suddenly catches such a noseful of scent that he knows the bird is very close by. There is no hesitation this time. Instead, he stops so quickly that he almost topples over, and stands there "frozen" until his master arrives.

Pointers are big, strong and built for fast running. They are among the handsomest of dogs, and, when properly trained for field work, one of the most remarkable.

Beauty, Brains and Courtesy

MANY PEOPLE WHO ARE FAMILIAR with a typical, purebred English setter believe that he is the most beautiful dog in the world. His smooth coat is of only moderate length on head, neck and body, but silky and quite fringed on the ears, legs and tail. He may be all white, or marked in combinations of white with smallish areas of black, tan, orange or lemon. From nose to tail tip he is as perfectly proportioned for speed, grace and endurance as a racing yacht. And anyone other than a pointer fan is likely to describe him as the best of all pointing-type gun dogs.

Two English setters will sometimes co-operate in a beautiful example of teamwork. They both may point the same game bird, or perhaps several birds huddled together on the ground in front of them. The closest dog probably catches the scent first and "freezes" solidly. The other may have caught it also, but just as likely he is only "backing" or "honoring" his companion's point without having any other proof that

With bulldog, terrier and some uncertain ancestors, the **Boston terrier** is a rather small dog with neat black and white markings and a less jowly look than the bulldog. Even though it comes from a fighting stock, the "Boston bull" is playful rather than belligerent.

Fox terriers were developed to drive the foxes out of their holes, where the larger hunting hounds could not go.

Beautiful **English setters,** with their fine "feathering," have long-haired coats of various color combinations. They are mainly white with spotted areas that may be tan, black, orange or lemon. Like other setters, they hunt admirably, often working well in pairs.

there are birds nearby. A setter may have to be trained to "back another's point" or he may do it naturally because his eyes tell him the other has found the game—and that he, too, had better stop.

An English setter is much more than just a wonderful bird hunter. He makes an excellent all-around companion dog for a single person, or for a whole family. Although he is large—about the size of a pointer —he gets along well in the house provided he has a good outdoor run every day. You could not ask for a more devoted, understanding and reliable companion. His only drawback is that his white hairs are noticeable when they fall out on dark rugs and carpets.

There are thousands of dogs, living in farmlands and wooded areas, that are excellent for their jobs, yet would earn only a frown at a dog show. These are the hounds, bred, kept and used for hunting and various chores. If anything, their care and breeding is even more closely watched than that of the show-winners; and more depends on their capabilities than on those of the purely "show" dogs. There are a great many varieties of hounds, and they are usually bred and trained for one particular type of hunting. Foxhounds are among the most common, and large packs are kept for the formal fox hunt with its corps of uni-formed attendants, uniformed participants, and its customs, rules and etiquette which must be meticulously observed. There is another type of hunting which is especially popular in the southern and central United States. Often called "hilltopping", this hunt consists of a mixed pack of foxhounds—belonging to the men staging the hunt—which course through the woods and fields at night. They usually chase a fox, but may take off after a raccoon, opossum, or other quarry. Meanwhile, the "hunters", usually local farmers and workmen, find a prominent hilltop, build a fire and warm themselves with fire and friendship as they listen to the hounds. Though the chase may lead miles and miles away, on a still night the baying of the hounds is not only audible, but individual dogs' voices can be recognized. The hounds are bred largely for the volume, timbre and quality of the voice. They are usually longer-legged than breeds such as the English foxhound, and they have a "rangier" appearance. The bloodlines are very jealously guarded, and the breeds often take the name of the men who originated them: Maupin, Tennessee Walker, Birdsong and Trigg are examples.

Fox hunting is responsible for the development of quite another type of dog. In the classical hunt, the hounds had to find the fox by scent, follow him by scent and sight, and have the speed and stamina to keep fairly close to him. When the fox "went to earth", the hounds were stopped completely. To deal with such a situation, a different type of dog was needed; one small enough—and brave enough—to go into the fox's burrow and drive him out. Thus was born the fox terrier. Many other terrier names—Staffordshire, Irish, Border, Sealyham, Bedlington, Norwich, Airedale, Lakeland, West Highland, Cairn, Skye, Scottish, Manchester, Kerry blue, Welsh and Dandie Dinmont—refer to the place of origin or to a human who had something to do with the breed. An exception to this "rule" is the name of the bull terrier, developed for the practice of "baiting" or harassing live bulls. Needless to say, any dog that would tackle a thousand pounds of irate bull had to have a lot of courage.

The Boston terrier was bred in Boston, from a bulldog-terrier cross-breed and a similar dog of questionable ancestry. It quickly became popular, and is one of the most popular breeds of all time among dog owners in the United States. The "Boston" or "Boston bull" is half the weight of a bull terrier, extremely well-mannered, and makes a very good apartment-dweller. He is amazingly quick and alert, playful, and a great "bouncer" for a toy held out of reach. This is one of the most naturally clean, well-mannered and affectionate breeds, and will likely always be popular.

The Strangest of the Hounds

NOBODY COULD MISTAKE AN AFGHAN HOUND for any other dog. The breed is at least several thousand years old—far older than many of the others. Yet even today he is completely different from all the rest and is likely to remain so. He is slim and very tall, with unusually long, silky ears and a coat that is long and thick everywhere except on his face and along his back. This is not the result of trimming or grooming, but the way the hair grows naturally.

The Afghan hound is believed to have originated perhaps 5,000 years ago, on the Sinai Peninsula at the head of the Red Sea, and at some unknown time he was introduced to northern Afghanistan, where thousands of years later he was rediscovered.

Even though it looks docile, the **Welsh terrier** is known for its ability to hunt down foxes, badgers, otters and other animals.

The Afghan is an early "sight" hound. Chances are that he was used to run down fleet-footed game in open country, relying much more on his keen eyesight than on any power of scent to keep on their trail. Even a modern Afghan gallops with a marvelous springiness and strength that gives him great speed.

One of the most difficult dogs for a person to buy or own, at least until recently, is the weimaraner. These talented dogs were bred by nobles of the Duchy of Weimar, and reached their present refinement in the early 1800s. They were closely guarded, and virtually nothing was known of them until many years later. Rigid rules have always governed their breeding; only choice dogs were bred, and any slightly imperfect pups were destroyed. Owners were limited to three or four dogs at a time, and had to be members of a "weimaraner club". If members voted against it, an outsider was simply not allowed to buy a dog, regardless of the money offered. In the United States these dogs stemmed from eight individuals imported by a Rhode Island sportsman who had been made a member of the German club. Weimaraner clubs are now found in America, and the same high standards are kept.

These striking dogs are often called "grey ghosts", and have been used to hunt birds, waterfowl, stag, boar and bear. They have, for all that, amiable dispositions and make good family dogs. An owner who might buy largely because of the lustrous silver coat and blue or gold-amber eyes may be surprised to find that he has also acquired an intelligent and devoted friend. The weimaraner is one of the few dogs to have lived in the White House in Washington; President Eisenhower owned one named Heidi.

Good Workers from the North

THERE IS A TENDENCY on the part of the general public to call any well-furred dog from the Far North a "husky". This is not accurate; there are at least four distinct breeds in regular use as sled dogs. It is easy to tell Samoyeds and Eskimo dogs from Siberian huskies and Alaskan malamutes; but the members of each pair may resemble each other and this can be confusing. Samoyeds are white or cream, as a rule, and never darker than biscuit. Eskimo dogs are a little bigger and more heavily built; but so far from being only white or cream, they may be black, golden brown—or in fact almost any hue that any dog ever was! The Alaskan malamute is called a "native" dog, and has lived in Alaska for thousands of years, perhaps even from the time of the land bridge to Siberia. His coat is of a wolflike grey, or black and white, with distinctive markings on head and muzzle. The Siberian husky is a smaller, lighter dog (and generally faster), with a softer coat. The coat may be white, black, or anything in between; and there may be masklike markings on the head. The eyes, surprisingly, may be brown or blue—even one of each!

One of the oldest breeds, the **Afghan hound** originated in western Asia thousands of years ago. Long silky ears and shoulder-length straight hair frame its unusual-looking face, which was considered by the ancient Egyptians to resemble that of a monkey.

The German **weimaraner,** a very specially bred dog, has high intelligence and makes a good hunter. From its coat, it is easy to see why its nickname is "grey ghost."

All these dogs, obviously related, are hard-working hunters, haulers, herders and companions for the far northern peoples. Polar explorations in many areas would have been impossible without them. Admiral Peary writes that they would "work till the last ounce of work was gone from them, then drop dead in their tracks without a sound." These breeds are still being used in the Arctic and Antarctic, and by many different nationalities around the world. People in temperate zones have discovered that, although these dogs can stand fifty-below-zero weather, they can be happy almost anywhere, and make excellent and unusual pets.

The Great Dane has been called the "Apollo of dogs". This breed, not much taller than an Afghan, but weighing twice as much, commonly exceeds a hundred pounds in weight, but in appearance there is no semblance of heaviness. Danes were bred to fight wild boars, which requires almost unimaginable courage, tremendously powerful jaws, and the agility to avoid slashing tusks. The Great Dane has all three. In addition, he has a combination of dignity and friendliness, besides intelligence and common sense. His qualities have always made him a much-appreciated bodyguard and companion, especially in the days of highwaymen and cutthroats. Great Danes have been used to guard mines in Africa, and one African chief so admired the breed that he offered two truckloads of ivory for one. These dogs may be brindled, with stripes, completely fawn, steely blue, solid glossy black, or white with black patches.

A little smaller, but even heavier, the Newfoundland is best described as "massive". These water-loving, good-natured dogs seem to make a habit of saving human lives. They like salt water and don't mind staying around boats and seacoasts, and thus are on hand fairly often when disaster strikes. Many times they have swum to a foundering ship through roaring breakers, towing a light rope to which a lifeline was attached. One such incident resulted in the rescue of no less than ninety-two persons, after other attempts had failed. The occasions when

(above)
Wolflike in appearance, the **Siberian husky** is, surprisingly, a very gentle and friendly animal. Its thick fur enables it to thrive in extremely low temperatures, but it is also comfortable in milder climates.

(right)
Eskimos have long used teams of **huskies** to travel across the frozen wastes. The dogs seem not to mind hard work and will push on to the limits of their strength.

a Newfoundland has pulled a drowning human out of the water are almost too numerous to count. As one might imagine, a dog of this size, and as tireless and fond of swimming in rough water, makes an excellent retriever. In fact, the entire breed of Chesapeake Bay retrievers was initiated by two Newfoundlands.

A Queen's Pet

IT WAS SOON AFTER THE YEAR 1100 when the dog which now has become the Pembroke Welsh corgi was introduced into southern Wales by immigrant weavers from Flanders. Little is known about his earlier history, although he is thought to have come from the same primitive stock from which chows, Pomeranians, and Norwegian elkhounds were developed. It is to this ancestry, perhaps, that he owes some of his ability to herd cattle and make himself useful in the guarding of his master's home and possessions. Corgis have even learned that they can nip a stubborn cow's heels and get away with it—*if* they drop flat immediately to avoid the kick that follows! There are two varieties, "Pembroke" and "Cardigan", from Pembrokeshire and Cardiganshire, respectively. The Cardigan migrated to the high country of Wales over 300 years ago. The Pembroke is marked by a higher body, more pointed ears and a shorter tail.

These low, powerful and astonishingly active dogs are naturally well-behaved. They like people, in a quiet sort of way, and are very easy to get along with. But there is a suggestion of mischief in their foxy faces and intelligent hazel eyes, so don't be surprised if a couple of them suddenly drop their usual dignity in a wild game of tag or in some other unexpected way.

(top left)
Meaning "dwarf dog" in Welsh, the **corgi** does indeed look stunted, with its short body and oversized head. A little larger than most domestic cats, it shares their habit of keeping clean by licking the thick hair covering its body.

(top center)
A wrinkled brow, large expressive eyes, and a tightly curled tail characterize the **pug,** a dog once popular with royalty of many countries. Originally from China, the pug remains true to type, hardly having changed at all in over three hundred years.

(top right)
Pekingese were long the sacred dogs of China, not reaching the Western world until as late as 1860, when the British brought them home. In Chinese, one of their names means "lion dog," which describes their imposing chests and fluffy manes.

Next to his intelligence, agility and very closely knit frame, a corgi's most interesting characteristic is his extremely dense, but not wiry, coat. While it gives him excellent protection against bad weather, it also sheds dirt and water easily. Some breeders say that you should never wash a corgi because he keeps himself clean. He actually does that, too, by licking himself all over as a cat does!

This odd Welshman, by the way, is a very popular breed among the members of the British royal family. When fully grown he weighs from twenty to twenty-four pounds and is ten to twelve inches tall at the shoulder. Not a big fellow, perhaps, but every ounce is topnotch dog!

The Little Dog of East and West

ALL OF US WHO GO TO DOG SHOWS, and many others who do not, are familiar with the appearance of a little Oriental with a wrinkled nose and a wonderfully soft, straight-hanging coat. But not too many people know where he came from, or know the strange life he lived hundreds of years ago.

From as far back as the year 800, and perhaps even earlier, the Pekingese was the sacred dog of China. The Imperial Family owned the oldest and best strains, and the penalty for stealing one of these royal dogs was death.

In those ancient days, the "Peke" had three names. Translated into English, these meant: first, lion dogs, because of their broad chests and thick manes; second, sun dogs, for their golden red coats; and third, sleeve dogs, because some of them were small enough to be carried around in the baggy sleeves of their owners' silken robes.

In the year 1860, when the British looted the Imperial Palace in Peking, four of these little dogs were found behind some of the draperies and taken back to England. One of them was given to Queen Victoria, and the other three to the Duke of Richmond and Lord Hay. These three were then used for breeding and, together with others brought in later from China, gave the breed its first real start in the Western world.

With such a background, is it any wonder that the Peke's personality is different from that of any other dog? He is dignified and stubborn, good-tempered, but afraid of nothing alive. He is much too independent to be turned into a mollycoddle and definitely prefers to stand on his own feet—even though they are tiny and he weighs only about ten pounds. Yet he is supremely devoted to his human family and can play with all the vim and joy of any dog.

A Breed That Used to Be Bigger

IN THE FLUFFY POMERANIAN you have a perfect example of how big dogs can be turned into little ones by many years of selecting the smallest puppies for breeding purposes. His early ancestors used to pull sledges in Lapland and Iceland; some of them herded sheep in other northern countries. Even a hundred years ago, long after the breeding-down plan started, some of the Poms in England weighed as much as thirty pounds. Today the ideal weight for show dogs is from four to five pounds.

In spite of this tremendous change in size, a present-day Pom clearly shows his distant relationship to some type of primitive arctic dog which was also the forerunner of the chow, Siberian husky, and the all-white Samoyed. They have the same upstanding ears and tremendously thick "double" coat which mark these much larger breeds, and if the little fellow is standing up, you can see that his tail is carried forward and close to his back, as are theirs.

In spite of his "toy" size, the Pomeranian is an up-and-coming little fellow, full of snap and keenly interested in whatever is going on. He is well built and active, too, and has plenty of courage. Few breeds have such a long list of correct hues. These include black, brown, chocolate, orange, red, cream, beaver, blue, orange-sable, and white with orange or black patches.

It is interesting to remember that when any kind of dog has been dwarfed by careful breeding its voice is much higher than that of its larger forebears. In fact, it is usually true that the smallest dogs have the shrillest barks.

Before the Pekingese and the Pomeranian came to be so popular, a miniature mastiff type of dog was "in vogue" to an amazing degree. Many ladies of fashion would not think of appearing in their carriages without a pug companion. Napoleon's Josephine, the Duke and Duchess of Windsor and the Prince and Princess of Monaco are among some of the more famous pug fanciers. The breed seems to have attained tremendous popularity everywhere it went; and then, for no apparent reason, interest in it lessened. But by 1957, after nearly disappearing around the turn of the century, pugs ranked seventeenth on the American Kennel Club's popularity lists. They have a long-legged look and a smooth coat, usually a light tan or silver, but occasionally they are

(top)
With short hair and many facial wrinkles, the **bulldog** matches the smaller, similar-looking pug in friendliness and affection. Yet the bulldog is over twice the size of the pug, weighing about fifty pounds when full-grown.

(above)
Like the Pekingese, the full-coated **chow** is an oriental import, having been one of the favorite hunting dogs of Chinese emperors. A chow can always be identified by the color of its mouth and tongue. Instead of the pink color common to most dogs, its mouth and tongue are distinctly black.

Descending from several breeds (including the spaniel, setter and pointer), the **Brittany spaniel** can well be proud of its mixed ancestry. It has made this breed a versatile hunting dog, skilled at both pointing and retrieving.

black. The muzzle is short, the face and ears are black, and the tail is carried in a tight curl over the back. Pugs are neat, affectionate and obedient dogs. They require little care and do well in both country and city.

We can only guess at the total number of dogs in the world, but the figure must be staggering. In the United States alone there are some 26,000,000—not including those in Alaska! Many of these are well trained, highly bred dogs from impressive bloodlines. The American Kennel Club recognizes 115 breeds, and registers about 500,000 studs a year. But by far the greatest number of dogs fall into the category of "just plain dog". Millions and millions of mongrel dogs live in all parts of the country, serving as companions, guards, shepherds, and perhaps most important of all, playmates of children from infancy to early teens. Aside from an obvious financial advantage—mongrels are either free or very inexpensive—there are those who swear that much-mixed breeds have better personalities and more natural intelligence than dogs which have been bred and refined primarily for appearance, with less attention to nose, sight, disposition and intelligence. This argument has gone on for many years and will probably never end, but there are points to be made for both sides. Certainly many mongrels are the equal of most highly bred dogs; they have distinguished themselves with feats of bravery in wartime and peacetime alike. And statistics show more human lives to have been saved and served by the world's mongrels than by any of the purebred dogs. The conglomerate pup has a definite place in the world. To a youngster his dog is the most important thing in the world, and he cares not a whit who or what his friend's ancestors may have been. Probably the most important things dogs do—whether mongrel or purebred—is to enrich the lives of their human owners.

It is little wonder that man has adopted and welcomed the dogs that have shared his life for 20,000 years or more; the list of advantages on the human side is enormous. As for the question: "Why do dogs put up with man?"—the only answer we can give is that dogs have a faithfulness and loyalty to the human race and are willing to serve it in any way they can, even sacrificing their lives in the process. Just why this is so we have no way of knowing; we can only accept and appreciate this happy fact.

CREDITS
Color photographs and illustrations appearing in this volume were supplied by the following: Photo Researchers, Inc.; The American Museum of Natural History; Armando Curcio; Doubleday & Company, Inc.; U.S. Department of the Interior, National Park Service; and H. S. Stuttman Co., Inc.

Cover illustration photographed at The American Museum of Natural History.

How will you grow today?

Go to school

Play in the park

Talk about your feelings

Read books

Sing songs

Ask for help

Be a friend

Explore the outdoors

There is so much for every child
in Dubuque to do to grow!

You can even feel mad and calm yourself by taking deep breaths.

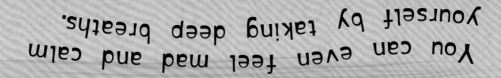

You can feel happy and ask for a high five.

You can feel sad and ask for a hug.

In Dubuque you can talk about your feelings!

or discover new ways to learn and play!

draw or paint in art class,

You can sing and dance in music class,

In Dubuque you can go to school!

You can ask a police officer to help you cross the street,

or, ask a teacher to help you read a book.

In Dubuque you can ask for help!

You can ask a trusted grown-up to tie your shoe.

or have fun on a swing
made just for YOU!

In Dubuque you can play in the Park!

You can run in the grass,

dig in the sand,

In Dubuque you can sing!
You can sing silly songs
in the bathtub, country songs in the car,
or rock-n-roll songs on your way to school.

Children's exposure to music and singing is linked to improved memory and ability to focus. Sing out loud to your child without worrying about being "in tune." Singing from the heart is inspiring and teaches your child confidence.

or grow beautiful
flowers in a garden.

In Dubuque you can explore the outdoors!
You can hike
on amazing trails, bike on miles of paths,

In Dubuque you can read books!

You can read about elevators that climb up the hillside, trolleys that travel around town,

or fish that swim in the river.

PUBLIC LIBRARY

In Dubuque you can make friends!

You can smile at someone new,

wave to a neighbor, or help someone in need.

Model appropriate social interactions for your child. Tell them how you meet new people. Ask them "who did you help today?"

There is so much every child in Dubuque can do to GROW.

CARNEGIE-STOUT FREE LIBRARY

DUBUQUE, IOWA
America's River

BRIGHT IDEAS!

Have your child find the "healthy growth icons" in the book
and then discuss how the activities on the page help you have a healthy brain, heart and body.

THIS BOOK BELONGS TO:

BE A HEALTHY YOU! IN DUBUQUE

Written By: Cynthia Wehrenberg • Julie Homb, LMHC • Abigail Degenhardt
Illustrated By: Tim Read

This project funded by a grant from MH/DS of the East Central Region as a component of the CARES Act, CFDA 21.019.

Visit us at: www.readdbq.org
Text and Illustration Copyright @2021 Community Foundation of Greater Dubuque

ISBN: 978-0-578-91619-4
Printed in China